About the Authors

This book was written by two beautiful women: Dr Olha Vorodyukhina and Mrs Jean Bertram.

Dr Olha

Dr Olha is a well-respected and experienced dental surgeon who spent most of her career specialising and advancing practice in medical aesthetics. Every year, she helps around 1500 patients to discover their beauty, a way of positive ageing and feeling confident about their skin. Her patients call her a magician, a fairy, a sculptor. She has an incredible talent to recreate a natural beauty in every face she treats.

Dr Olha also shares her exceptional knowledge about facial aesthetics with other medical professionals as a lead medical aesthetics trainer with Cosmetic Courses (the longest and largest established training providers in medical aesthetics in the UK).

Jean Bertram

Mrs Jean Bertram has been working alongside Dr Olha at her Angels Twelve clinic for the last five years. She is the heart of Dr Olha's business, although her official title is Clinic Manager. Jean is an absolutely unique person: she lives and breathes her job and is so passionate about it. She ensures that every customer who walks through the clinic door has the best experience; she is genuinely interested in patients' stories and lives. Jean has been a witness to hundreds of lives changing, transformation and results that were delivered by Dr Olha.

With love
Dr Olha & Jean

Beyond the Mirror

Dr Olha Vorodyukhina
& Jean Bertram

Matador
Unit E2 Airfield Business Park,
Harrison Road, Market Harborough,
Leicestershire. LE16 7UL
Tel: 0116 2792299
Email: books@troubador.co.uk
Web: www.troubador.co.uk/matador
Twitter: @matadorbooks

ISBN 978 1 80313 237 2

British Library Cataloguing in Publication Data.
A catalogue record for this book is available from the British Library.

Printed and bound in the UK by TJ Books LTD, Padstow, Cornwall
Typeset in 11pt Minion Pro by Troubador Publishing Ltd, Leicester, UK

Matador is an imprint of Troubador Publishing Ltd

What do real women do to boost self-love
and self-esteem?

This book was written with the aim of empowering
women and helping us connect inner and outer beauty.

Contents

Introduction ix

1 Dr Ohla and Mrs Jean Bertram Stories 1

2 What Does the Word "Cosmetic" Mean to You? 11

3 Staying Safe 31

4 Treatments 40

5 Customers' Stories 91

References 124

Introduction

In the modern world of today, how women feel about themselves often affects how they live, and let's agree, we all have good and bad days in our life.

But beautiful, strong, inspirational ladies have never lost face regardless of how high or low they feel. Many wonder what the secret is.

So here we are, trying to crack the puzzle in this book.

What is the secret of those who seem to have it all in life and always look gorgeous?

Beyond the Mirror is a book written by incredible, real women. It is not just to be read as a book or as a story, but the purpose of the book is to help as many women in the world as possible to discover their confidence, the natural beauty in them, and to be able to say *yes* to self-care and self-love.

A good sense of self-esteem is how real women enjoy things around us and feel personal validation. This feeling comes from within, and the higher it is, the further in life you can go. However, often it is assaulted by outside circumstances. It is hard for women to feel good about themselves, especially when they are constantly absorbing negative messages. This is why *Beyond the Mirror* was created. So that it can guide women all over the world into a sense of self-worth and by loving themselves it will show where true success is found.

Women who believe in themselves tend to be more confident, and it shows in how they walk, talk, and dress. But how do you get to this place? Self-love for women can mean many different things, whether it is learning how to work in a man's world, improve self-esteem, or deal with the "perfect self-image". Every woman deals with some aspect of this and must find a way to overcome it so it doesn't end up holding her back.

Beyond the Mirror is a book for all women. Our aim is that the concepts and recommendations contained within this book are clear, simple and easily accessible regardless of whether you are completely new to skincare, medical facials and other treatments or you are an experienced patient who has it all. When it comes to self-care, there is no one-size-fits-all approach.

This book is not like any book you will have read before: it incorporates everything all modern women need to know to make an informed decision about healthy skin, a healthy look, positive ageing and beautification.

In today's busy modern world, we see cosmetic clinics that offer Botox and filler treatments overtaking hairdressing, beauty salons, and certainly some dermatological clinics. In an unregulated industry, you can easily get trapped and be misled. But you only have one face and it has to represent you all your life.

So, when you first start to think that maybe it's time to do something just for you, then you should read and enjoy *Beyond the Mirror* before searching on the internet for answers. That should put you firmly on the right path. The book will hopefully, through true experiences, help you to overcome the negative media messaging around cosmetic treatments.

This book has embarked on the journey of empowering women of all ages and educating them on what is available, what is safe for them, what choices they have, how to avoid regretful mistakes and lastly, but most importantly, this book will be sharing the real stories of the patients whom we've cared for and those currently in our care. So, allow us to welcome and lead you to the "new you" journey!

Chapter One

Dr Olha

This is me... and this is my story...

My name is Dr Olha. I'm a dentist, aesthetic practitioner, and business owner. I'm a mum of *three* and a wife. I love my life and what I do, helping so many look beautiful and feel confident.

Now, how did it all start? Well, like all of us, it started with the moment I was born. I was born in Ukraine into a medical family. In fact, I'm the third generation of medics in my family.

Being a very spiritual person, I strongly believe in destiny. When I look back, it seems that everything that has happened in my life, all the experiences I've gained, were given to me from above for a purpose. And this purpose is what I do today: help thousands of women every year unlock their beauty potential, discover positive ageing, and, through improving their appearance, increase their self-confidence, self-love, and make their world a better place.

So, let's go back to my roots. My parents were first-year junior doctors when I was born. They were committed to continuing their further education, like everyone in our family. Therefore, I was raised by my wonderful grandparents from two years old until I was six.

My grandma was a teacher of the Russian language and literature, and my grandpa was a doctor. He was a doctor on the front line during the Second World War and, as a child, I used to sit on his lap, and he would tell me all the stories about war battles. I loved it so much. In my country, we call war doctors like him "doctors with a capital letter".

My grandma was from a noble family who unfortunately lost everything and everyone during the war. At the age of sixteen, she was left alone in a concentration camp. The one thing that stayed with her and helped keep her going was her positivity and incredible self-belief. My grandma was able to maintain her love for the finer things in life that she was accustomed to as a child despite the hardship that she was put through in her later life. She then passed this passion on to me. As a little girl, I was a glamorous little thing – hats, dresses, bags, and shoes – a love for these lavish things began very early on.

Sadly, my grandma passed away from cancer when I was five, and I still remember that day now. My grandpa asked my parents if I could stay with him as I suppose it helped him keep going at the time. Then, I learned more about medicine as, often, he would take me with him to work.

I was a clever little gem, too: reading and writing all before starting school. I was even learning the German language and writing letters to my parents.

At the age of six, I went back to live with my parents and started school (in Eastern Europe kids go to school at six). I started Latin American dancing at the same time as primary school, where I did well and studied hard.

But during secondary school, it was a different story. Throughout my secondary schooling, my parents had a lot of ups and downs with me. I got my education completely *free* and, looking back now, I didn't appreciate this at the time. How foolish I was. But none of us are perfect, right?

I'm extremely lucky to have parents like mine, who would always step up and steer me in the right direction when I needed it. I was pushed to reach my potential, and that is one big, important lesson that I learned from my parents, and one I will teach to my children.

You don't know at fifteen/sixteen what is best for you in life. Well, at least I didn't. Having been raised in a medical family, I almost had no choice but to become a doctor when the time came to make this decision. So, to be slightly different, I decided to be a dentist. My true passion (which I had for many years – since primary school) to become a doctor was overridden by that stubborn teenage mind urging me to do something different from what my parents said, and so I applied to dental school. Not the worst choice, I suppose, but, as I mentioned earlier, I am a strong believer that everything in life happens for a reason.

Today, the combined experience of mathematical proportions gained through dentistry and my perception of beauty through working in the fashion and beauty industry has given me a competitive advantage to do things differently from other practitioners.

The fashion and beauty industry – how did I forget to mention this? While I was in my final year of dental school, I started my first business. And it was not dentistry. It was a modelling agency. Completely different, right? But it was a total success, and I sold this business when I moved to the UK. Having my business allowed me to work part-time as a dentist. It was a pretty awesome experience for a student: top shows, VIP parties, fashion designers. I was even on billboards and made the front cover of various fashion magazines.

So, how did I end up in England? I met my future husband, Laurence, in Ukraine one day, and my life changed forever. I always say, "when you know, you know". No years of dating. We got married within a year of meeting each other. I remember when I returned from visiting him in England after six months of dating and told my mum that we were getting married and I was moving to England. No mother wants to hear that their only child is emigrating, but thankfully I have a very supportive and strong mum, who is always there for me, yet lets me make my own decisions.

I moved to England in 2009. This country made me a much stronger person. I'm extremely grateful for that. However, I needed to start everything from scratch: do all my dental exams, do vocational training, etc.

My husband, who is a sport and exercise medicine consultant, developed an interest in facial aesthetics. I found this subject so fascinating and close to my heart and soul, too. So, obviously, I was fully involved in his new hobby, and then I took it over. Some of the patient stories here go all the way back to when Laurence was treating them.

So, while I was studying in the UK for my dental qualifications, I was helping my husband to establish an aesthetic business. By the time I passed all my exams and received registration with the General Dental Council, I knew facial aesthetics would be the right career path.

So, back in 2013, I booked my foundation courses with Cosmetic Courses, and I never looked back. Since then, I have attended hundreds of courses, training sessions, and lectures. Being an educator myself, I strongly believe that in order to be the best practitioner you can be, you can never stop learning.

Believe it or not, I know what treatment a person needs, what area of the face we need to address first, how much product I will need, and how many sessions of treatment after only a few minutes of assessing their face. I guarantee natural results to my patients.

My closest and dearest colleague told me one day, 'You don't know how great you are.' Honestly, I appreciate this, but I have a different opinion about that. The moment we think we are great is the moment we die as a specialist and don't push ourselves any further. I always want to deliver even better results to my patients, and I want to constantly improve my skills. And the reason I wrote this book is to educate even more women on what options are available for them to feel happy and confident about themselves.

Some people may say they made themselves happy and confident. I'm not one of those. I have people in my life who, without them, I would not be where I am today. I'm grateful to my grandparents, who gave me a great foundation, my parents, who pushed me and pointed me in the right direction when I needed it, and my supportive husband, who is the rock in my life and my best friend. To my beautiful children, who are my blessing; I have been reborn with each of them, stronger, more determined, and motivated each time. And, of course, I could not do what I do without my incredible team of people who are experts in their fields. Like Andrew Carnegie said, "take away my factories, but leave my people and soon we will have a new and better factory". I feel exactly the same about my team at both clinics, Angels Twelve and Cosmetic Courses.

Jean Bertram

This Is Me!

Yes, I know it's a line from a fantastic musical, but when I was thinking about writing my story in this book, it immediately came to mind as I have been asked to share my very personal experience from the beginning of my journey to achieving and maintaining a positive approach to looking and feeling good throughout my ageing process.

I'm sixty-two years old now, and it makes me happy when others question my date of birth – don't get me wrong, I'm not saying that I look twenty-one again, but what I am saying is that I think I look the best I possibly can for my age and it makes me happy and confident in my day-to-day life.

About seven years ago, I was recommended to see Dr Olha after chatting with a work colleague who had seen her in the clinic. My lower face was my concern, and although I wasn't happy with my under-eye area, I did think that only surgery would correct the problem. How wrong could I be? I didn't make the call straight away. I had to think about it for weeks before I decided to take some advice. On my first visit, I felt completely at ease, with no pressure to "go for it" there and then – I asked lots of questions, and still, I had to go away and decide if aesthetics was the right path for me or if I should have medical facials and skincare. I made another appointment, discussed things further, and decided to try a Fire and Ice Facial before going ahead with anything else. At this point, I was still quite scared of aesthetics; would I like it? Would it hurt? And all the usual feelings I'm certain everyone goes through before making a start. After more deliberation and with butterflies in my tummy, I decided to go ahead and make a tiny little step with 1ml of Juvederm in my marionette lines. It didn't hurt, and although the difference was minimal to everyone else, it gave me the courage to carry on because this was something I had decided to do "just for me", and I loved it.

Over the years, I have had multiple treatments, with each enhancing the results of the previous. Under Dr Olha's guidance, I've tried and tested more advanced procedures, and together, we've reviewed regularly what works for me because we are all individuals, and what you see on others is not always what's right for you, going back to my title "This Is Me!". And after thinking that my eyes were something I had to live with, I now, without surgery, have the most amazing results without puffiness, baggy lines, or dark circles!

For regular clients at the Angels Twelve clinic, you will have probably realised that "this is me", Jean. I'm lucky now to work closely with Dr Olha and help make our customer journey an individual experience. For people who are still thinking about it, I am happy to share my experience with you all.

My advice to anyone who is considering any kind of skin treatment, or investing in any skin product to use at home, is to book an online consultation with Dr Olha to see what's right for *you*.

The above was the article that appeared in local media and, because of the responses, made us realise how people are influenced by unnatural faces on television, awful horror stories, pictures in the press and online, and needed to hear from genuine people how nothing negative has happened to them. Aesthetics are not just for celebrities.

They are for normal people who have normal lives and simply want to age beautifully for themselves.

I am lucky enough now to be a part of a very experienced team working towards helping everyone to understand their skin and how it can improve over time, with the possibility of delaying or even reversing some of the obvious signs of ageing. However, for me, this hasn't always been the case, and I'm sure that everyone reading this book will have wasted time and money using cosmetic skincare products with little or no effect other than making a huge dent in their bank balance and filling up their drawers at home.

I had quite an unusual childhood in the early 1960s because my mum went to work, which was very rare and not always accepted within my friendship group. They had mums who stayed at home and looked after the house and their husbands while the men went to work and the pub. But what I do remember is that my mum was very glamorous. She was the first person on our street to bleach her hair and the first person to wear tights when they came out. How strange it is to look back when you think of the progression over the years and where we are now that such run-of-the-mill things would cause quite a stir. I think my mum's sense of independence and her love of everything she achieved has been with me throughout my life, and I'm sure she has been the motivation behind me always wanting to look my best and trying innovative treatments to help me feel confident and strong. I would like to think that my mum would have been the first in line to try aesthetic treatments, and I thank her for instilling her attitude in me.

My background is customer service, and you would only have to walk through the door of our clinic to realise that the whole team is committed to making everyone feel as comfortable and special as they possibly can. Another factor towards putting my experience in print is to share some of the conversations I have had with our clients about how they felt on their first visit and how they feel now.

Even as a young mum with two little girls, I would always make an effort and take the time for myself and enjoyed make-up and experimenting with different looks. Although good advice wasn't readily available or affordable to me at the time, I believed even then that the earlier you start to have a good regime, the more you benefit later in life, although at the time I couldn't even imagine being forty, never mind being sixty-two with a forty-year-old daughter! It seemed like forever away and that I had all the time in the world. Sadly, as we know, time goes so quickly and the ageing process starts from your mid-twenties. We don't have all the time in the world, and all of a sudden, your skin changes, and new plans have to be put in place to make you feel and look your best.

I've been married for forty-four years, and I am lucky to have my husband as my best friend, who has supported me throughout what seems like more than a lifetime. He would never put any pressure on me to change anything and is always happy if I'm happy. This goes back again to the title "This Is Me", and the message to everyone is to do what makes you feel good, and if looking your best makes you happy, then do it for yourself, and other people will benefit from your self-confidence. Needless to say, my two daughters, and now my twenty-one-year-old granddaughter, are as dedicated as I am to their two-minutes-a-day skincare regime, so the legacy continues, and even my nine-year-old granddaughter loves to help herself to my make-up drawer at home.

My background in customer service has helped me a lot, from selling shoes when I first left school to heading a team of thirty people to achieve their goals. I have always maintained that it is important to spend time with your customer to help them make the best choices when buying shoes or purchasing something life-changing. I love to learn, and the job I have now is my passion. I feel that in many respects, it is the job that has challenged me the most and allowed me to connect with people who love to look and feel their best. Whatever their age, motivation, and roles in life are, they all come to see us for the same result. An important aspect of what we do is the "getting to know you" phase of our appointments, where everyone's individuality comes through. It is so interesting to find out what motivated people to take a step towards ageing beautifully.

Chapter Two

What Does the Word "Cosmetic" Mean to You?

It probably brings to mind creams, oils, powders, lotions, and a variety of other beauty products. "Cosmetic" is a word that conjures up images of beauty, and who doesn't want to be beautiful? The word "beauty" no longer refers solely to women; men are just as concerned with their appearance and are constantly striving to look their best!

Most of us will feel better if we look attractive; it is proven that it increases our self-esteem if we are confident in the way we look. A mixture of elegance, confidence, and charming personality. As you get older, the changes that happen on your face reveal your age! But hold on, that is not the case anymore. People have mastered the art of remaining young and beautiful thanks to the different beauty and medical treatments available on the market these days.

Simple facial treatments will make you feel refreshed and give your face a rest. This can range from home remedies to trips to the beauty salon. You have the choice of spending money and being pampered, or saving money and treating yourself at home! You may be wondering how a standard beauty salon facial can restore your youth. The ordinary treatments involve the application of a high-quality moisturiser, mask, serums, and SPF to protect against UV rays, all accompanied by a relaxing massage. You may choose to go for an alternative at-home treatment, using your grandma's recipe and what you have in your garden or what you find in the local shop or supermarket, for example, cucumber to remove dark circles and refresh tired eyes. You'll be shocked to learn that potatoes and onions, as well as lemons, bananas, and honey, play a role in facial treatments. Well, let us tell you, this foodstuff is better than nothing, but that is not what you need if you want to discover flawless skin that doesn't need any make-up coverage.

If you're truly wanting to achieve a healthy, glowing, even complexion, then you may want to take your time and receive professional advice on correct skincare and medical-grade results-driven facials. This is usually available at specialist clinics: medical aesthetic clinics, private dermatologists, and cosmetic centres. You can look at the chapter four treatments in this book to find out more about what options are available to you. For example, as well as topical facial procedures, cosmetic treatments also include surgical and non-surgical aesthetic treatments. Non-surgical cosmetic procedures are injectable treatments and include, but are not limited to, Botox and fillers, PDO thread lifting, skin booster injections, radiofrequency treatment and medical microneedling.

These treatments help not only to reduce wrinkles and facial lines but also help to restore lost plumpness and volume, or even reverse some of the negative emotions that our face can convey as we age. For example, you may look sad because you have downturned corners of the mouth, or tired because you have hollowness and puffiness under the eyes, or even old and saggy due to the loss of definition in the jawline and the development of a turkey neck, or angry due to frown lines. Non-surgical treatments can also help treat acne, acne scarring, open pores, and pigmentation, among other things.

Medical aesthetics combines anatomy, physiology, pharmacology, mathematics, mental health, dermatology, and dentistry and is therefore an absolutely unique art and must not be compared with any other specialty. Practitioners need all of the above skills to be a specialist in this field of expertise. Remember, *you*, our potential patients, are about to trust us with your most treasured possession: *the face*.

Rapid advancement in product development, improved training standards, and endless educational information available should help anyone considering any cosmetic treatments. We still often need to overcome many barriers before making a decision to book an appointment for a consultation. So in this chapter, we want to focus more on the motivation behind medical aesthetic treatments.

Dr Olha's famous expression "every patient is a new book" tells the story. So, when choosing who to trust with your face, you should ask your practitioner how many books they have read.

Our gorgeous patients have taught us so much. We're amazed and privileged to be a part of their journeys, to hear and read their stories, and to fully understand their motivation behind the treatment. And those beautiful stories of unique people have inspired us to write this book.

Let us just say this from the beginning: the motivation ordinary people like you and us have is not to look like an

A-lister or to make the cover of a magazine. Our beautiful patients are mums, wives, grandparents, single, married or divorced, or maybe they are brides-to-be. They may have had the toughest time of their life fighting cancer, suffered some facial deformities, and been self-conscious about their looks, or they may have simply decided to positively age. But they all have the desire to feel happy and confident when they look in the mirror, to look at their reflection, smile, and say, 'Yes, this is me, and I'm worth it.'

Over the last ten years, our patients have taught us invaluable lessons by sharing why they receive treatments, how it makes them feel and what effect it has on their lives. We've seen women who didn't like their reflection in the mirror discover self-love and confidence again. Our patients tell us how they get questioned about their age and how many people compliment them on their looks. Some say that their partners are very proud of their motivation to look well and admire their desire and discipline for self-care.

This makes our job so special, as what we do has a much greater impact than just restoring the youth of your face. We have all heard that age is just a number. We can feel as young or as old inside as we like, wish, or feel. But ninety per cent of the time, this reflection that we see every morning in the mirror determines and dictates how we feel.

So, let's look at some facts and statistics. Let's also listen to expert advice on what drives our motivation to have the treatments and what obstacles we all overcome on the way to beautification and the positive ageing journey.

These are some facts that are worth knowing. Since 2013, the number of cosmetic procedures has risen by forty-seven per cent worldwide. According to the study, seventy-two per cent of facial plastic surgeons have noticed a rise in patients under the age of thirty.

The study claims that because they grew up with social media, millennials – those born between the early 1980s and the late 1990s – became obsessed with self-care and therefore have an increased demand for plastic surgery procedures. Social media has not only made getting your body tweaked professionally less taboo, it has also served as a motivator for individuals to undergo plastic or cosmetic surgery.

According to the report, non-surgical procedures such as Botox, fillers, microneedling, and non-surgical rhinoplasty, accounted for four-fifths of cosmetic treatments in 2018, and doctors said that one of the main motivators for patients was the need to look better in selfies.

But, because of this self-care component, millennials aren't generally opting for major cosmetic procedures; instead, they're more concerned with staying youthful and looking as natural as possible.

According to the 2018 AAFPRS report, more patients are seeking preventative, cosmetic procedures. Millennials, unlike past generations, aren't waiting until they're older to get Botox and fillers to look younger; they're more likely to undergo treatments in their twenties and thirties to maintain their youthful appearance.

According to the survey, plastic surgery patterns are changing away from "overly enhanced looks", like Kylie Jenner's lips circa 2016, and towards a more natural appearance. However, almost all AAFPRS members believe that celebrities continue to manipulate cosmetic procedure patterns.

Why Do We Make These Decisions?

Physical appearance is a vital part of personal identity, and it has a long history of influencing people's self-perception. While innate preferences such as symmetry and a small waist-to-hip ratio direct women's perceptions of attractiveness, the sociocultural context may also influence perceptions of attractiveness. According to the Tripartite Influence model's three main sociocultural influences – peers, parents, and the media – beauty norms are reinforced and transmitted. Internalisation of beauty values (when an individual accepts society's beauty expectations and participates in behaviours to attain them, this is known as internalisation) and appearance comparison (people judging and specifically comparing themselves to others based on how they look) are two factors that mediate these influences.

It is suggested that if a person internalises beauty stereotypes about looks that she/he cannot live up to (e.g., those portrayed in the media or reinforced by parents) and/or participates in appearance comparison (e.g., with peers), this may lead to body image issues such as body dissatisfaction. The media has a significant impact on society's perceptions of body image, such as what body type one should have and what one should wear, largely through the dissemination of advertisements about the "ideal body" in magazines, newspapers, and television. The impact of media messaging on women's body image has been studied using conventional media such as television and magazines for a long time, but over the last decade, newer types of media, such as social media, have had a major effect on our views and self-image.

Social Media's Influence on Body Image

The media's emphasis on physical appearance is arguably more convincing than ever in today's society, particularly among younger people and through newer forms of media such as social networking sites (SNS). Instagram is a free social media site that allows users to edit and upload images and videos through a smartphone application. Instagram concentrates on images rather than written text, unlike other social media platforms such as Facebook and Twitter. Social media platforms' visual, picture-oriented nature, especially Instagram, encourages users to look at and comment on the photos that others post on their profiles. Other users' physical appearance will influence whether or not they look at and comment on these photos.

Ringrose discovered, for example, that British teenage girls often receive feedback about their physical appearance via their social media profiles. As a result, how we are viewed on social media will affect people's perceptions of our appearance and, in some cases, inspire them to take action. People can, for example, make minor changes to their appearance, such as dyeing their hair, changing their clothing, or changing how they apply make-up. In other cases, such as those caused by cosmetic modifications, the improvements can be more long-lasting and dramatic. These changes can have significant ramifications in such situations for their psychophysical function, as physical changes can positively or negatively impact well-being.

The use of social media is common in the United Kingdom, and it is an integral part of young adults' everyday lives. According to the Office for National Statistics 2020, social networking is the most common internet activity among adults aged sixteen to twenty-four years (ninety-six per cent) and twenty-five to thirty-four years (eight-eight per cent). However, the impact of social media is pervasive. More body image issues and eating disorders have been linked to increased social media use. According to other studies, Instagram is one of the most harmful social media sites for young people's mental health and wellness (The Royal Society for Public Health 2020). Similarly, Brown (2020) discovered that looking at Instagram photos of sexy celebrities and colleagues has a negative impact on women's mood and body image. These results indicate that excessive use of social media sites, especially picture-based sites, may be detrimental to certain people's body image and psychosocial functioning, such as lowered self-esteem and an increased risk of depression and anxiety.

Consistent with the growing popularity of social media, an increasing number of young people are undergoing cosmetic processes, from 17.2 per cent in 2018 to 25.2 per cent in 2020 (American Society for Aesthetic Plastic Surgery 2020). The "maintenance, repair, or enhancement of one's physical appearance by surgical and medical techniques" is what cosmetic surgery entails. Reconstructive surgery is a surgical operation that is performed to restore function or natural appearance. It is also used to treat irregular body structures such as those affected by trauma or infection. Cosmetic surgery, on the other hand, is performed on natural body structures in order to enhance appearance and shape (American Society of Plastic Surgeons 2020). Cosmetic surgery has become a common way to improve one's appearance, with the British Association for Aesthetic Plastic Surgeons (2020) reporting that about thirty thousand procedures were performed last year, and is a popular culture industry that is heavily affected by changes in our society. According to the American Academy of Facial Plastic and Reconstructive Surgery, social media picture sharing has increased surgery requests. Rhinoplasty, Botox, and facelifts were the procedures most likely to be requested as a result of social media influence, implying that what young people see online may influence their decision to undergo cosmetic procedures. Similarly, a study found that Facebook, YouTube, and Instagram are popular among cosmetic surgery patients for information about procedures, such as practice information, before and after photos, and competitions. Despite the growing popularity of cosmetic procedures, the social and psychological factors that affect attitudes towards cosmetic surgery have yet to be thoroughly investigated.

Does Social Media Have to Take All the Blame?

The world we are living in today is changing dramatically. But let's be honest with ourselves. Cosmetic treatments have been around well before the internet came along.

In fact, seventy per cent of patients at our clinic don't use social media. Or they use it very infrequently.

What drives their motivations? Here are some examples of what we have been told:

'I do this for myself because I want to look the best I can.'

'I do it for myself as I'm tired of looking tired.'

'I do it for myself as it is my time now. I sacrificed a lot for my husband and kids. Now it is my turn.'

There is a lot of educational information available for patients. People also speak more openly these days about cosmetic treatments. Friends and family who want to age beautifully could have already had some treatments and so could give you good cosmetic recommendations.

So here is the answer to the question of motivation: personal recommendation or hearing the story of your friends is a real driving power behind cosmetic treatments.

Decisions, Dilemmas, and Questions We Face before Taking the First Step

In this part of the book, we aim to answer your questions about embarking on cosmetic treatments by discussing how we made our decisions to journey towards positive ageing. I know that may sound a bit like a cliché, but to be honest, everyone we spoke to had the same choices to make and came to many different decisions based on their own individual feelings.

Of course, we have questions, doubts, and hear this inner voice in our head many times before we consider cosmetic treatments. Should we or should we not? We know that; we have been there ourselves. Moreover, thousands of our patients have been facing the same dilemmas too, and we want to put your mind at ease.

I suppose that in everything we do in our lives, we always have to think carefully and make the right choices. In some little things that we do along the way, we may make the wrong choice, but it doesn't always have a massive impact on our life. For example, "shall I buy another pair of shoes?". If you fancy them, you can afford them, and they make you happy, then go for it and enjoy. That's not going to make a huge difference to you or anyone else, and let's face it, life's too short not to take a risk now and then. You can always "be good" tomorrow if that's your choice.

However, when it comes down to how you want to age and how you want to feel about yourself, that's a different story altogether. So, we have to ask ourselves, what do we want to achieve and how can we possibly get there? Through all of the magazine articles, social media influencers, reality TV, and other people's opinions on ageing "gracefully", how can you possibly know what is good, bad, or even a dangerous path to tread?

Decisions, decisions… there's always something to consider, especially while planning our busy schedules. Rushing around making sure everyone else is OK, and giving little thought to the strong and independent person you are, you're the one that keeps it all together, so how can you possibly have the time or money for yourself? Well, that's a thought – *how can I fit it in?* We know that there are only so many hours in a day and that, most probably, every single minute is allocated already. But consider, what would really happen if you took the occasional hour out of your week to make you feel good about yourself? Would our days seem less stressful if we just stepped back a little and re-evaluated what we see as a priority? Would our world collapse if we just relaxed for an hour once in a while and just looked at how special and talented we actually are? We all deserve some "me" time. That's what keeps us going. Hopefully, that answers the question, "do I have time?". Just think about it for a while and read on.

Then, obviously, other things will pop into your head, cost not being far down the list of considerations, because there's always something that takes up the money every month – how can you possibly afford what you're thinking of at the moment as a luxury? This is the next question you will probably ask yourself. There are always kids' shoes or clothes to buy – let's face it, they grow so fast and time goes by so quickly, then the car starts playing up, and that's another expense… what about the decorating? But the big question is, what about *you*? What we're trying to say is stop putting everything else first, look in the mirror, and believe you're worth budgeting for, whether it is by investing in medical-grade facials and at-home products prescribed specifically for you, or taking the next step and enjoying the benefits of expertly placed dermal fillers and Botox. It's up to you to take the first step. It doesn't need to be expensive. It's about making the small changes that will make a big difference from the outside in.

The next on our list is the big one – *will I like it, and will it change my natural appearance?* This is an easy answer for us because we see the positive results for everyone on a daily basis, so it would make things simple if we could just say, yes, of course, you will like it, and no, it won't change your natural appearance, but that would be unfair of us to expect you to believe without the honest stories of our lovely ladies in chapter five. That's the whole purpose of *Beyond the Mirror*, to help you to see, believe, and understand the subtle, natural changes to the faces of the volunteers who offered to help us and you by sharing their stories.

You'll see that not all of the pictures in the book are of ladies who have chosen to have injectable treatments. They make time for themselves by enjoying their facials in the clinic, complemented by a quick and effective two-minutes-a-day at-home skincare routine. If the correct treatments and products are used, then fantastic results can be achieved, so don't assume one size fits all, it absolutely does not, and having received the right advice, our clients feel good about their appearance and themselves. Others have chosen the injectable treatments we offer in-clinic following a comprehensive consultation process. We hope you'll agree that whatever their story or motivation behind the decision to positively age, they all look like a fresher and younger, but a very natural, version of themselves. Collectively, they all agree that caring for yourself can change your life and the lives of those you care about.

Hopefully, by sharing real client experiences, we will answer the question of whether cosmetic treatments will alter your natural appearance, and we hope that you will take the next step knowing confidently that, with the right practitioner, you can look and feel the best possible you.

What about, *will it hurt?* This comes up quite regularly, as you can imagine, in fact right up to the point you take the first step and experience the treatment yourself. "I don't like needles" is another very common comment we hear from most people. Well, who does like needles, really? I can't imagine that anyone would say that they are their favourite thing, can you? So, let's try to ease these thoughts by turning the negatives into positives. By the time you are ready to have the treatments, you hopefully will have ticked most of the boxes and answered the questions most important to you: you will have made time, you will have researched your practitioner, you will have had a consultation and considered the costs, and you will have decided now is the time to make a start. You should feel apprehensive but comfortable in the clinic and confident that you are ready to go ahead. Nothing about your appointment should ever feel pressured or hurried, and enough time should be allocated to revisit your consultation and address any further questions you may have at this stage. We can assure you that nothing we do causes too much discomfort; a topical anaesthetic would be liberally applied and given enough time to make you feel numb. The needles we use are very fine, and you can always close your eyes during the treatment. No pain, no gain is the well-known saying, but if administered correctly, you will be pleasantly surprised at how little you will feel during the procedure. Don't worry, you'll soon forget the butterflies in your tummy and smile in the mirror at the results.

There are lots of aesthetic practitioners out there, *so how do I choose?* There are a few simple rules to follow when researching which clinic and which practitioner will give you the best advice while working in a safe environment. Ideally, you would be recommended by someone you trust who has had experience of aesthetic treatments, where you can see the results for yourself. That being said, if you book for a consultation at a recommended clinic and you don't feel comfortable with either the advice or the standards, then walk away and look elsewhere. Save Face is a good place to start your research. They are a company that endorses aesthetic clinics and checks for high standards in every aspect of client care. This is a voluntary inspection clinics can opt for where they are inspected regularly by Save Face so that they can appear on their website and can be found in a local area's postcode searches.

Save Face never endorses non-medical aesthetics and continually campaigns for stricter regulations around this industry to prevent anyone who is not medically trained from administering any kind of non-surgical procedure. To achieve these regulations, which we also fully support, would be a huge step forward for the United Kingdom to catch up with other countries in the fight to stop dangerous facial disfigurations and scarring caused by non-medical professionals. Unfortunately, it is always these horror stories that are reported in the media, rather than fantastic photographs of natural-looking, cosmetically enhanced faces, again giving the industry a bad name.

So, Save Face is a great way to help you choose which clinics to look at, then check the websites to see what treatments are offered, what the credentials of the practitioner are, and, importantly, look at the reviews from their clients to see what real people are saying about their experience and their results. You should also be able to see some real before and after photographs of existing clients who will have given their express permission to share their images to help other clients who are doing their own research. If you see the same photograph on more than one website, they are probably stock photos purchased for advertising purposes, so steer clear of these clinics if they claim them as their own work. Talk to the receptionist and book either an online consultation or a face-to-face meeting with the doctor, whichever you prefer. Consultations do not usually incur a cost, but a deposit is often taken to secure the booking, which can then be redeemed against any treatment you decide to go ahead with or refunded if no procedures are carried out. Check this at reception before you go ahead, along with the cancellation policy before booking an appointment, as you don't want to pay until you are sure you've found the right place to go. In short, Save Face, safety, experience, testimonials, and medical qualifications are the things you should check before considering making a start. And at your first visit, you should feel safe, welcome, happy, relaxed, and fully informed.

How do you move forward if other people close to you are advising against you having any treatment? This is something we hear in the clinic regularly, "my partner says I don't need anything doing". Fantastic! They love you and find you very attractive without any help at all, just the way you are – that's a great place to be, but how do you feel? That's the question you have to ask yourself, would you be having this discussion at home if you hadn't already considered the fact that you might feel better about the way you look with just a little, subtle assistance?

Personally, I, Jean, am in a relationship where we have been together for years. Of course, my husband would never say anything hurtful or insulting to me. He has seen me fat and thin, blonde and brunette, pregnant and a new mum. Then, getting older, he has always supported my decisions but was very unsure at first when I talked to him about not liking the lines around my mouth and feeling a little saggy and considering having some treatment. I realised then that I was stepping into the unknown, and it was not only a little scary for me, but it was quite worrying for him as well because, of course, he didn't think I needed anything done. Now, I think that he is secretly very proud that I want to look the best I possibly can for my age. I am also very proud of the way I look and feel, obviously with a little help from my friend, Dr Olha.

So, you have to consider your loved ones' feelings and understand that they may be scared or worried that you won't look like yourself. Explain that you have taken all precautions to find a perfect practitioner who fully understands that you just want to look a fresher, younger version of yourself without changing your appearance. Explain how it will make you feel better, not different, then go ahead, and they will also feel the benefit of your confidence boost.

Is it wrong of me to want to look my best? We know that this sounds like a completely ridiculous thing to ask ourselves when considering any sort of treatment, but it is one that crops up in conversation. *Should I grow old gracefully?* Where did this statement ever come from if it's to be used in the negative sense? The answer is most definitely yes, you should grow old gracefully, by looking after your health, well-being and the way that you look and feel about yourself. This should be a positive statement and something to focus on, not just mean to give up and get old.

Every advertisement on television around health will encourage us to keep active for our strength, flexibility, mobility, and mental health. A healthy diet also helps us to keep fit and alert, with little treats along the way as an act of rebellion – we can't always be perfect and, going back to what we said earlier, making little bad choices along the way is what life's all about, and they likely won't have any long-term detrimental effects to you or anyone else. In fact, "a little of what you fancy does you good" is one saying that we all like to hear. It's not about being vain or self-absorbed. It's about making the most of the one life we have and enjoying every day along the way. Wanting to look good plays a huge part in how we feel as well as a healthy lifestyle. Isn't it a fantastic idea to make the most of the options available to us now to look and feel confident in our appearance? This could be a new skincare routine to brighten and refresh, or it could be a few little tweaks to lift and tighten your face. Whatever is right for you is the right thing to do. Don't listen to the negatives. Just grow old gracefully and beautifully.

What will others think of me? Firstly, let us say that you would be shocked at the number of ladies who have chosen to have a little help here and there along the way, but you would never know as some ladies choose not to tell their little secret. Maybe because they don't want to be judged, or maybe they just want everyone to believe that they are lucky enough to age positively with no help at all. You can choose which you want to be – you can shout out how fabulous you feel and how proud you are that you are investing the time, money, and effort in making yourself feel and look good; after all, it's your choice, and you're doing it for you, so why not tell the world? If you want to be quietly confident, then that's completely up to you, just give everyone a little smile and say thank you when they tell you how well you look. It's your secret to keep and should never be shared by any clinic without your agreement in writing.

What if something goes wrong? Firstly, let us say that although all procedures carry an element of risk, it is very rare – if the products used are genuine and the protocols are followed – during treatment that you would suffer any adverse reaction to any type of aesthetic treatment. If you see any pictures in magazines, newspapers, or on social media of disastrous results from lip fillers, always read the story behind the article and don't presume that this would happen to you. If you follow the rules and choose carefully where to go and who to trust with your face, then the risks of complications are very, very small. The media love a good story, and because aesthetic treatments are so unregulated in this country, it leaves the industry wide open for attack from outside sources. We've read stories about lip filler parties in people's own homes. How can that be medically acceptable to anyone? It's not fun or a party game. These are potentially life-changing treatments that can, under these circumstances, leave you disfigured forever.

We've seen adverts for treatments in tattoo studios, which is also quite shocking, where tattooists also use toxin and dermal fillers without any medical training. Beauty therapists, while often quite skilled in their field of expertise, are not qualified medically to administer non-surgical treatments. Sadly, the list goes on and on. Each article we read is just as shocking as the ones we've read before – we still can't quite understand how anyone would risk their reputation or clients' faces just to make money. And we definitely can't understand why anyone would consider letting someone untrained loose on their face.

Through the medical clinic we manage, we have, of course, come across some of these problems caused by non-medical people. Sorry, I can't call them professionals because if they were, they wouldn't do it, and I have had to correct the work carried out in error. That's why we constantly campaign for more regulations in our industry, while in the meantime advising everyone considering their treatment to choose carefully, check the credentials of the aesthetic practitioner, check the reviews, speak to the doctor as many times as they need before they go ahead. If, on the rare occasion, there are any complications under these circumstances, then your medical professional will know exactly what to do, and they will have everything to hand to deal with any situation.

We hope that this chapter has helped you relax and appreciate yourself in a way that you've never done before. Also, that we've helped to answer some of the thoughts and doubts you may have regarding your own individual journey. The questions we have asked and answered are the most common ones on people's minds; they are the ones we are asked the most, and later you will read through our clients' stories to help you further understand what a difference, if done properly, a good skincare routine or facial aesthetics has made to them. Some of the stories are funny, and some are a little sad, but collectively they all decided to enjoy their ageing process and make the most of every minute feeling great.

Chapter Three

Staying Safe

Welcome to the short but very important chapter three. How to stay safe. Not be disappointed. Get results that you would like with medical cosmetic treatments.

Aesthetic medicine does not save lives, but it can certainly change them. By doing your research and choosing the right practitioner for you, these changes can be very positive and lead to a fresher, younger, happier *you*.

If you make rapid decisions, are mislead by social media advertisements, or try to save money on something priceless (your face), you could be left disappointed, self-conscious, and often unhappy with the results.

Although cosmetic treatments are rarely life-threatening, more and more often, we see that these treatments can be life-altering when performed incorrectly. An unregulated industry makes it easy for anyone without any previous experience or medical qualifications to treat patients, take their money, and mislead them, taking naïve patients to the dark world of cosmetic treatments.

So, please trust our honest and expert advice – you have *one* face and it deserves the *best*. In this chapter, we will not only give you a guide to what to look for when you are searching for your new aesthetics physician, but we will also provide you with a guide on how to choose your aesthetic physician and what questions to ask.

We have all seen the many horrifying pictures in magazines where injections have gone wrong. But this can happen with topical treatments, too: burnt faces after chemical peels, excessive bruising after a microdermabrasion treatment or medical needling, and even reactions to incorrectly prescribed skincare products: redness, itchiness, and mild chemical burns. Believe us, you don't want anything to ever go wrong on your face. But if it does, you want it to be resolved as soon as possible and receive all the help you need from the treating doctor or aesthetician.

So here we go!

Step One

Do your research. Personal recommendations are the best way to go in the medical sector and personal care. You may be surprised, but your dentist, GP, or even hairstylist will often know a good medical aesthetic specialist whom they will not hesitate to recommend. Maybe your friends and family will share their beauty secrets. It is good to ask for practitioner contacts, especially if the person who has had treatment looks well and fresh.

Don't trust just a recommendation alone. After receiving a recommendation, look at the clinic website and read any feedback, etc. It is advisable to check multiple platforms (Google, Trustpilot, Facebook, Save Face, Glowday, Doctify, RealSelf) when researching a clinic.

Check practitioner credentials (nurse, doctor, dentist). You can check their registration on the GDC, NMC, and

GMC websites. What is their level of expertise in aesthetics? Have they completed one day of training, or do they have years of experience? Do they have any postgraduate qualifications? There is absolutely no question that – when it comes to injectable treatments – injections should be administered by a medical professional.

But what about your skin treatments? You would like your therapist or aesthetician to be careful, gentle, and knowledgeable, right?

We would advise you to apply the same approach as when you were searching for your doctor: personal recommendations and reviews.

We would personally want to go to a medically led clinic, where a multidisciplinary team can perform your treatment under professional medical guidance. Ideally, we would like a therapist to have a Level 3 or 4 qualification.

Did you know that in the UK, you can complete a one- to two-day course on anatomy and physiology without any previous beauty or medical background and then straight away learn how to inject fillers and place PDO threads? Ouch, even the thought of the above gives us goosebumps while we're writing it.

The world of aesthetics is absolutely *mad* out there, and the ugly reality is that the only person who can protect you is *you* by choosing reputable, experienced, and safe clinicians.

Expert Tip

When you do your research, look at qualifications, professional registration, experience, recommendations, reviews.

Step Two

Book your consultation. Don't walk into the clinic in rose-coloured glasses. Check the cleanliness, what the team looks like, how they greet you.

How do they look? Natural, well, fresh with no obvious signs of enhancements, e.g. overfilled lips, etc. That is a good indicator.

Can you tell if they have had work done? Does their look frighten you? Maybe it is just what they want and like. Everyone has a personal preference. But it also may be a sign this clinic is not right for your needs.

Consultation is the most important part of your treatment process. It can take, on average, about thirty minutes. Your clinician will usually check your medical history, your history of past treatments and your skincare routine. They will also examine your face and they may do a photo assessment. Sometimes, they may be required to use a skin analyser to see deeper layers of the skin and possible underlying problems.

In our clinic, the clinic consultation is always a dialogue. We want to know our patients and get as much information as we can in order to provide them with the best possible plan.

We will always prioritise patients' concerns and work towards the goal to correct them. But we will also educate our patients on available options and advise the best option for them.

Some practitioners hesitate to recommend and advise as pointing out negative factors and negative changes that could occur to your face might be quite daunting.

Here is our point of view on this: we're experts who can see beyond your skin. We know what will work and what will not for you. And if you are open, of course, to our professional advice, then we're here to lead you on this beautiful journey. And the most important thing is to be honest with our patients.

The patient education process is a big part of our consultation. We don't want you to leave confused with what is available and where to start. We would like you to leave the consultation with a full understanding of what caused the changes on your face/skin and be excited about your next step. This next step will be taking time to think and discuss your options with your family or booking an appointment for your treatment.

During your consultation, the practitioner usually will show you their portfolio of work, as well as advise on risks associated with the proposed treatment. The cost of the treatment also should be provided.

Most experienced practitioners will provide patients with a treatment plan that they can take home and think about.

Expert Tips

On what questions you should ask during the consultation:

1. *What product will be used?*
2. *Why did the practitioner choose this product?*
3. *How long will the recovery time be, if any?*
4. *When will you see results?*
5. *What options are available if something goes wrong?*
6. *How long will the results last?*
7. *What sort of maintenance will be involved?*

Step Three

Think. Take your time and think. Review your expectations and manage your desires. Discuss your plans with friends or family if you feel that you need support. You may want to come for a second consultation if you have any doubts or unanswered questions.

We always encourage patients to think and take some time between consultation and treatment, as we know it is a big step for many. It's stepping into something unknown. As much as we know that you will love your journey, you need to be confident in your decision and be happy to take this journey of beautification and positive ageing.

Step Four

Treatment day. Are you excited? Are you nervous? Is it mixed feelings? We see it every day in the clinic. Some patients are very excited, some relaxed, others extremely nervous, very anxious.

On the day, the treatment itself is just a small part of the process. It will start with filling in consent forms, medical history, and pre-treatment photos will be taken. The practitioner will explain the treatment process again, step by step. We will make sure all your questions are answered. If your treatment requires pain relief, then it will be provided (topical numbing cream or injection of a local anaesthetic). Some practitioners work with assistants who can provide further support to the patient during treatment.

Most injectable treatments require face mapping, or what you may have heard of as marking the face. It is considered good practice as the practitioner is always more accurate with injection placement.

Many non-surgical treatments have very little or almost no recovery time. This means you can go back to your work and day-to-day activities almost straight after treatment. We can apply a sterile foundation after your treatment if you have to be somewhere straight away.

Step Five

Aftercare. Verbal and written advice will be provided to you after the treatment. Most clinics will provide you with an out-of-hours telephone number that you can call if there are any problems.

Step Six

Review. Each patient is offered a review appointment following the treatment to ensure it was successful and they are happy with the results. The review can be done by video call or face to face. It is important for a few reasons:

1. Sometimes we may need to do minor corrections at your review appointment, as the best approach in medical aesthetics is to undertreat rather than overtreat. This means if you had Botox treatment, you might have more movement than you expected and we may need to do an extra treatment at review. If you had dermal filler treatment, we might need to balance the symmetry and add more product or help the product to better integrate by massaging the area. Keep in mind any correction can only be done at a face-to-face review.

2. If you are completely happy with your treatment, it is still very important to attend your review appointment as we will do a photo assessment, compare the achieved results together and plan your future treatments or maintenance.

We would advise you to always check with your practitioner whether the review appointment is included in the cost of your treatment or whether it involves an additional cost. Usually, this should all be advised during your initial consultation and clearly stated in the treatment plan.

If you are a regular patient at the clinic and receive a maintenance treatment that you've had in the past, in this case, review appointments are not necessarily essential, especially if you are happy with the outcome.

Most caring clinics always will check in with all their patients about how they feel a few weeks post-treatment and if you need a review, it can always be arranged.

Expert Tip

It is important to have full access to (and support from) the clinic and clinician if you have any worries, need some reassurance, or develop a complication in exceptional circumstances.

Step Seven

What next? Maintenance. You are looking in the mirror and you smile, happy to see your beautiful reflection. No more tired-looking eyes and frown lines looking back at you.

We're sure you won't want to go back to the old version of yourself. In fact, we're confident this is the case as most of our patients say the following:

'I prefer how I look now.'
'Who is this person on the before-treatment photo?'
'I'm a year older, but I look five years younger.'
'I look my best since I've been coming to see you.'

So, how do you maintain this look? It is easier to maintain what's been achieved in the restorative stage of the initial treatment. Depending on your age and any skin problems, we will see you once every four to twelve months and advise the right treatment at the right time. There are a few examples of a comprehensive treatment plan in medical aesthetics available for your attention in chapter four.

Please note: all treatment plans provided are just a guide to give you an idea, but treatment plans are bespoke for each patient and you can ask your practitioner to provide you with one during your next consultation.

Chapter Four

Treatments

In this part of the book, we take a look at the different treatments available at medical aesthetic clinics. We will explain the pros and cons of each and we will give you our personal, professional opinion about these procedures.

We can't help but start this chapter with our favourite treatment – maybe it is your favourite too – dermal fillers. It is by far the number-one treatment in our clinics. We strongly believe that hyaluronic-acid-based fillers are our best friends when it comes to beautification and positive ageing.

As you know from reading this book so far, there are different components to the ageing process. With the help of dermal fillers, a knowledgeable and experienced practitioner can restore lost volume, create contour and definition to the face, and improve skin quality.

The best thing about dermal fillers is that when they are done correctly, no one will know why you look so good, but everyone will notice your fresh, beautiful face.

The second-best thing is that we can work at your own pace; how quickly you want to achieve your result is completely up to you.

In some cases, patients decide to have the whole treatment in one go to achieve an instant result that can be long-lasting and easily maintained. Others prefer a more cautious approach and have their treatment in stages.

And because our dermal fillers are our number-one treatment compared to other non-surgical procedures, we have dedicated a large chunk of this chapter to them.

Dermal Fillers: What Are They?

Dermal fillers are soft tissue implants that are injected into the skin and can be permanent, semi-permanent, or temporary. They're utilised to replace volume loss due to ageing, disease, or illness-related bone, fat, and collagen loss. They can be applied in a variety of aesthetic areas of the body, but the most common are the face and hands.

Types of Dermal Fillers

Silicone and other permanent fillers are rarely utilised in the face. They may appear to be the most cost-effective option at first. However, as the face changes shape, a well-placed filler today becomes a not-so-well-placed filler years later. It is difficult to remove a permanent filler, so they are now becoming outdated in the modern aesthetic medicine world.

Semi-permanent fillers can last up to two years and have a variety of applications in the face: Radiesse, Ellanse and Sculptra are examples. Radiesse is a calcium hydroxylapatite suspended in water. It's employed in deep tissues where bone loss has occurred for precise implantation. It's especially effective along the jaw bone, nasolabial folds, and the orbit's inferior rim (eye socket). Sculptra and Ellanse are made of polymerised lactic acid.

Dermal Filler Based on Poly-L-Lactic Acid-Ellanse

Injectable poly-l-lactic acid (PLLA) has become a popular choice for restoring a young appearance to the ageing face since it was approved for cosmetic usage. This minimally invasive process involves the addition of long-lasting volume to the area where it is placed without the need for individual wrinkle treatment. However, because of the potential for side effects from inappropriate application of the medicine, physicians must adhere to consensus recommendations in order to achieve the best possible patient outcomes. The purpose of this chapter is to provide an overview of the history and injection instructions for PLLA, with a focus on its application for facial volumising.

Poly-l-lactic acid is a synthetic material that is biocompatible (meaning it is safe to use in the body) and biodegradable. It's been utilised in medical equipment like dissolvable stitches for a long time. Poly-l-lactic acid products are categorised as "collagen stimulators" since their principal technique for smoothing fine wrinkles is to assist your skin in regenerating natural collagen – the filler gel itself disappears after a few months. Poly-l-lactic acid is commonly used to repair deeper face wrinkles, with benefits lasting up to two years.

By far, the fillers most often utilised in the face now are temporary fillers based on hyaluronic acid. For a while, collagen filler was very popular, but it also had more side effects and the possibility of allergic reaction. Hyaluronic acids (HAs) have mostly taken the place of collagen. Hyaluronic acid is present in our body, joints, and skin and is a naturally occurring chemical. HAs are safe, have a minimal risk of adverse reaction, and last for six to twelve months on average. There are many different brands of HA fillers available, but we only will name the most reputable ones and those that are used in the medical aesthetics field with great medical research behind them – Restylane, Juvederm, Maili, Bolleterro, Teoseal, Aliaxane – in this book.

What Are the Benefits of Dermal Fillers?

A person's face may begin to look drawn and haggard for a variety of reasons, including weight loss and age-related changes. Collagen and fat compartments on our face help young faces look full and firm, but as we get older, our skin's collagen levels decline and volume loss and volume redistribution takes place. Fortunately, there are a variety of non-surgical procedures that can be performed to restore a patient's youthful appearance.

Dermal fillers are one of these procedures and are becoming increasingly popular for a variety of reasons. Dermal fillers offer instant effects, so you don't have to wait weeks for the swelling to subside before seeing the treatment's results. Recovery time is usually minimal; patients may experience a little swelling and bruising at the injection site, and slight redness in the treated area is possible, but it will go away quickly.

When you have dermal filler treatment with a skilful and experienced practitioner, the final result can be comparable to surgical results. However, the emotional attributes behind the treatment and the fact that you have no recovery time or risks associated with surgery make dermal filler treatment the number-one treatment of choice for many men and women.

Hyaluronic Acid Fillers: How to Prepare

Patients considering HA fillers should avoid blood thinners (consult with your doctor) and alcohol for twenty-four to forty-eight hours before treatment. This will lessen the likelihood of unwelcome bruises.

It is advisable to have treatment at least two weeks before any important occasion. Make sure you ask your practitioner about all possible questions you have prior to the treatment.

What to Expect During a Filler Treatment with Hyaluronic Acid

A needle or cannula is used to inject hyaluronic acid fillers. (However, your injector will still need to use a needle before using a cannula.) Because a cannula's tip is blunt, it cannot pierce the skin.

In terms of the actual physical sensation of injection, most fillers on the market are pre-mixed with lidocaine, so the area becomes reasonably numb with little pain during treatment. The entire treatment takes around thirty minutes to an hour, depending on where the filler is administered.

Time to Recover

The majority of patients have little or no recovery time. Hyaluronic acid strengthens the structure of the skin while attracting water molecules, resulting in increased skin volume and hydration. Some of the outcomes will be visible right away, while the final result may take a week or two to appear. The results can last anywhere from a few months to several years, depending on the HA filler type utilised.

Aftercare

After a filler treatment, you should consume plenty of water and stay away from alcohol for at least twenty-four hours.

Because alcohol has been shown to aggravate bruising, toasting with a glass of wine to your new filler just after the injection may result in less-than-ideal results, sorry!

You should not have any facial treatments for at least two weeks after the dermal filler procedure and avoid laser treatment for four weeks. Dermal fillers don't like extreme temperature changes; therefore, you need to avoid hot baths, steam rooms, hot tubs and high-intensity exercise for seven to ten days after the treatment.

Risks and Side Effects

Although dermal fillers are quite safe, like any medical intervention, they are associated with certain risks. The biggest risk is when dermal fillers are injected into the blood vessel and can cause vascular occlusion. If it is not immediately addressed and resolved, it can lead to skin necrosis and even blindness. Special emergency medication, hyaluronidase, can be used in the treated area to dissolve filler and reverse the side effect.

Recent research also found that dermal fillers can cause an immunological response. This rare side effect can happen when a patient has a compromised immune system or when they are fighting infection. This may cause worries clinically, from mild swelling of the fillers to the formations of hard lumps (granulomas) that can cause facial disbalance and disfigurement. In most cases, an immunological response self-resolves without any treatment. A few patients may need a short course of steroid medication and some may need fillers to be dissolved.

Overview of CO2 or Carboxytherapy

This treatment was called "miracle gas" by Brazilian *Vogue*.

Stretch marks, dark under-eye bags, cellulite, residual fat deposits after liposuction and small areas of localised lipodystrophy can all be treated with carboxytherapy treatment. Carboxy treatment is based on the premise that by injecting CO_2 into a specific region, the body will respond by supplying more oxygen to that location.

Carboxytherapy is a medical procedure that involves injecting medicinal carbon dioxide gas into the subcutaneous tissue with a needle. It removes fat cells, increases blood flow, enhances skin suppleness, and decreases cellulite dramatically.

Carboxytherapy's History

Carboxytherapy, commonly known as carbon dioxide therapy, has been used in royal spas in France for over eighty years. Patients who soaked in the carbon-dioxide-rich thermal waters on a regular basis had faster wound healing. It was later discovered that exposing the skin to carbon dioxide enhanced blood circulation as well as the texture and flexibility of the skin.

Since then, the devotion to carboxytherapy has risen year after year, demonstrating the therapeutic modality's significant benefits. The mentioned "gas injections" are used in balneotherapy to treat joint difficulties and poor blood circulation in the lower limbs (ischemic disease) and diabetic patients' skin, as well as some patients with systemic vascular illnesses and heart disorders (bradycardia, low blood pressure). However, in the last decade, this therapeutic modality has gained popularity as a one-of-a-kind procedure that may be used in dermatology, aesthetic dermatology, and anti-ageing medicine.

The approach is widely advocated as a procedure that is less invasive, easy to tolerate by patients, and offers maximal effects without the risk of adverse effects. The approach is being studied at the University of Siena in Italy, as well as the University of Milan and Pavia's Center for Microangiology and Microcirculation, as well as clinics in Austria, Hungary, the Czech Republic, and Slovakia. Many countries throughout the world advocate and implement the CO_2 method (Australia, Korea, Singapore, and South America).

What Is Involved in the Treatment?

The treatment area will be cleansed with antiseptic before the process begins. Before the injection, a topical numbing cream can be applied to the injection site. A tiny needle will be introduced into the subcutaneous tissue. Carbon dioxide diffuses into surrounding tissues from the injection site. The extra CO_2 causes the body to deliver more oxygenated blood to the area, which improves circulation and the skin's general appearance.

Carboxytherapy addresses issues like:

- Cellulite
- Stretch marks
- Scars
- Skin tone/texture disparity
- Treatment for eye bags and dark circles
- Psoriasis
- Rejuvenation of the skin
- Raynaud's syndrome
- Early stages of hair loss

Can It Be Used in Conjunction with Other Treatments?

CO_2 therapy can be effectively used with treatments such as:

- Platelet-rich plasma (PRP)
- Mesotherapy
- Botox injections
- Dermal fillers
- PDO threads

It's important to remember that, when used in conjunction with botulinum toxin, the effects can (but not always) be reduced. Therefore, CO_2 therapy is advisable to be completed first.

Excellent results can be produced when PRP is used in conjunction with CO_2 therapy. This treatment combination can provide excellent results for hair loss and skin rejuvenation. Your doctor will advise you on the best treatment combination for your needs and goals.

The Benefits of Carboxytherapy

Carboxytherapy is a very natural way to approach skin rejuvenation. It does not involve any chemicals and only helps your body with its natural recovery and healing process.

It is also an affordable treatment with minimal recovery time. There is no evidence of adverse reaction, and no long-term side effects or complications were reported following CO_2 therapies.

For best results, a course of treatments is recommended, anywhere between five and twenty sessions. Results are long-lasting but require maintenance every six months for certain conditions.

Overview of the Plasma Pen

Plasma Pen, often referred to as fibroblast, is a relatively new cosmetic procedure that is swiftly gaining favour. It's a non-invasive treatment for a variety of skin problems like sagging, wrinkles, and elasticity loss. Fillers or plastic surgery have traditionally been used to correct these concerns, but the FDA-approved Plasma Pen provides a non-invasive option to the surgery.

The History of the Plasma Pen

The process involves emitting a very tiny electrical arc from the tip of a handheld gadget without actually touching the skin. A plasma arc is created when a mixture of oxygen and nitrogen is formed just above the surface of the skin, vaporising it and tightening the surrounding area instantly. Collagen begins to regenerate within days, crusts form and flake off, and smoother, tighter skin emerges.

It simply has an effect on the epidermis and improves the appearance of the skin. Plasma Pen treatment can be considered an alternative to plastic surgery in some cases and may be used on a range of body parts.

What Are the Most Common Areas to Be Treated with a Plasma Pen?

- Tightening of the eyelids (baggy lower eyelids and excess upper eyelid skin)
- Crow's feet
- Imperfections on the skin (sunspots)
- Scarring, particularly post-surgery scars and acne scars
- Stretch marks

- Skin tags
- Skin elastosis (wrinkling), although other methods can be considered to treat this that offer a more holistic approach with less recovery time
- Tightening sagging stomach skin caused by pregnancy
- Smoker lines (any lines and wrinkles around the mouth)
- Neck skin tightening is a procedure that tightens the skin around the neck

How Long Do the Results Last?

The effects should last as long as an invasive procedure would (average three to five years). Plasma therapy, like all non-surgical and cosmetic procedures, has a semi-permanent effect because it does not prevent future ageing. However, depending on the area treated, the favourable outcomes should endure for years. The favourable benefits of treatment will be visible as soon as the first session is completed, with the optimum results appearing after four to eight weeks. For best results, two to three sessions are recommended six to twelve weeks apart.

What Is the Duration of the Treatment?

Treatments normally take one to two hours, depending on the area we treat.

Time to Recover

On average: five days.

One to three days

There will be little scabs where the doctor has placed dots with the pen. The majority of patients say they don't hurt, though they may itch as they heal. Following treatment, your doctor will prescribe products to help you deal with this problem. Between days two and three, the scabs will lift and deepen in colour. It is important to leave then exfoliate and not try to pick them.

Four to five days
The scabs will peel off, leaving little pink dots on the skin. The itching and irritation stop at this point.

Day five and beyond
The surface of the tissue continues to recover. New collagen production, on the other hand, is still in its early phases. The average person will see an improvement in the target area by day seven. The full effects will be visible in eight to twelve weeks. Some clients' findings may be delayed due to health conditions or medications.

What Is the Duration of the Effects?

Plasma Pen results can last anywhere from two to five years, with an average of three years.

PDO Threads' History

Surgical facial rejuvenation extends back to 1911, although polydioxanone threads are a relatively recent development, dating back to 1998.

Non-absorbable materials were used in the early thread lifts, and despite their effectiveness, they were not popular because of their permanence. The invention of dissolvable PDO thread lifts drew attention due to their long-term results.

What Exactly Is a PDO Thread?

Unlike standard thread lifts, which leave the sutures in the skin, a PDO thread lift uses polydioxanone threads, which are biodegradable and have skin-strengthening properties.

Polydioxanone is a colourless, totally biodegradable synthetic polymer. PDO strands are compatible with human physiology and fully dissolve into the treatment region after four to six months, unlike typical thread lift sutures.

Until recently, patients seeking treatment for facial skin laxity had to resort to invasive facelift procedures. PDO thread lift treatments were created as a non-invasive skin-tightening option and are the most recent cosmetic procedures utilised to effectively renew and rejuvenate saggy skin.

The minimally invasive process can minimise indications of ageing, improve skin texture and elasticity, and stimulate collagen formation.

Why Is PDO Thread Lifting Popular Now?

One of the most significant advantages of PDO thread lifting therapy over standard facelift treatments is the non-invasive procedure's shorter recovery time.

Traditional facelifts need one to two weeks off work for rehabilitation, with the first three to four days requiring constant attention from a medical team.

However, with a PDO thread lift, recovery time is considerably reduced and rather easier. Though you may have some discomfort, swelling, and redness right after treatment, these symptoms usually only require one to two days of rest, making it easy to get back to your routine.

Thread lifts are low-risk procedures and less invasive in comparison to surgery.

What Can PDO Thread Lifts Help With?

PDO thread lifts are now available in a wide range of methods and can treat a wide range of aesthetic concerns. PDO thread lifts can help with a variety of conditions, including:

- Sagging jowls and drooping cheeks, which can be treated with skin tightening;
- Wrinkles around the eyes, on the forehead, on the cheeks, and around the lips;
- Neck skin that is sagging and double chins.

Threads are even used for stimulating hair growth factors. PDO threads are not only limited to the face and neck areas but can be used on the body as well: upper arm, abdominal and chest tightening, knee lifts.

Collagen and PDO Thread Lifting

The treated area's evident improvement will last for more than a year. This is because PDO treatments promote the development of collagen in the skin, which is an important part of keeping skin appearing young and healthy.

Collagen stimulates the production of growth factors in the skin, allowing wounds to heal and giving the skin a soft, voluminous appearance. Our natural collagen production decreases as we age, and our skin thins, resulting in extra skin and wrinkles. The impact of volume loss that results in sagginess exaggerates with ageing.

Because PDO thread lifts provide much-needed collagen structure to aged skin, they offer a long-lasting rejuvenating effect. A PDO thread lift supports collagen stimulation, which leads to a progressive and continuous increase in skin firmness.

When the threads are inserted, the body's healing mechanism kicks in, attempting to "expel" the foreign item and heal the area. This results in increased collagen formation and enhanced blood flow to the area, thereby tricking the body into repairing the condition of the treated area on its own.

PRP: Overview

The idea behind platelet-rich plasma treatment, commonly known as the vampire facelift, is that the body's natural healing power can reverse the ageing process. It works by placing growth factors in the particular location where we require the skin to rejuvenate and repair itself. As such, plasma treatment involves harvesting platelets from an individual's body and injecting them into skin areas with a problem. Usually, blood is drawn from a patient's arm and allowed to separate. The red blood cells separate from platelet-rich plasma, which is rich in growth factors (proteins that heal damaged or injured skin).

History

Platelet-rich plasma therapy has been on the scene for some years in neurosurgery, orthopaedics, dentistry, and sports medicine to treat injured muscles and ligaments, skin lesions, as well as pain problems. The success of the procedure in medicine led to the development of a cosmetic procedure – a vampire facelift.

What It Involves

As earlier mentioned, vampire facial treatment involves harvesting platelets from a patient's blood and injecting it into injured skin areas, thus various nicknames like "Dracula therapy" and "vampire facelift". Prior to the procedure, blood is drawn out from a patient and placed in a centrifuge to allow the platelet plasma to separate from the red blood cells. The platelet plasma (rich in growth factors) is injected into the skin (face), where it is believed to reduce wrinkles and fine lines.

Once the platelet plasma is injected, it releases growth factors, causing the surrounding cells to increase in volume; one such cell is the fibroblast cell that is responsible for producing collagen. Another cell stimulated during the procedure is the preadipocyte cell, a cell that converts into a fat cell, thus filling out lines on the face. The procedure is performed around the mouth, nose, eyes, and backs of the hands, as well as the knees, to give the skin a radiant look.

Benefits

Skin rejuvenation (fine lines, improves skin appearance, restores natural glow) and stimulation of hair growth (treatment is effective at an early stage of hair loss). PRP is effective when combined with other treatments such as dermal fillers and PDO threads.

Which Areas Can Be Treated?

Face, neck, hands, scalp, décolletage.

Recovery Time

The vampire facial may require very little recovery time, and most people can go back to their normal activities the following day. Some redness and bruising may occur, which will disappear within days or a week's time.

Why It Is Popular

The treatment is not just another overhyped cosmetic procedure; it is effective as it has a long history and research behind it. PRP is widely used in the medical field to treat muscular-skeletal problems (it is widely used for intraligament and intrajoint injections). Celebrities like Kim Kardashian, Bar Refaeli and Rupert Everette are said to have undergone a vampire facial procedure.

Anti-Wrinkle Injections

Ageing is accompanied by the appearance of two types of wrinkles:

1. Dynamic wrinkles, caused by muscle activity, for instance, frowning, which causes wrinkles between the eyebrows, or crow's feet, which is a result of smiling.

2. Static wrinkles are associated with loss of volume, for example, deep lines around the lips and nose (nasolabial lines) and forehead.

Botox injections are designed to treat and prevent dynamic lines by suppressing muscle activity.

What Is an Anti-Wrinkle Injection?

It is naturally occurring proteins that are injected into the muscles and work as muscle relaxants. There are three main Botox manufacturers in the world market, the Allergan product, Botox; the Merz product, Bocouture; and the Galderma product, Azzulure.

What Does the Treatment Involve?

The procedure involves small injections, which usually cause only a minor sensation of discomfort. At your request, a topical anaesthetic can be applied to the skin prior to the treatment, or we can use a CoolTech medical device that significantly reduces the tenderness during the injections.

What Is the Result?

Smooth lines and no wrinkles - you will be looking natural and fresh. When you are treated by an expert, they definitely avoid giving you that "frozen look"! You will notice the results between five and ten days after the treatment and it lasts approximately three to four months.

Side Effects

Mild discomfort and redness can occur at the site of injections, but this usually fades the following day. Occasionally there can be minor bruising to the skin.

Which Areas Can Be Treated with Botox?

The entire face can be treated with Botox and it can also be used on some body areas successfully. The most popular treatment is on the upper face: treatment of forehead wrinkles, glabella (between the eyebrows) and around the eyes. Also, Botox can be used to treat sagginess around the neck area, a treatment known as a Nefertiti neck lift, and for jaw contouring and slimming the lower part of the face - Botox will be injected into the masseter muscle. Botox is also a very effective treatment to reduce the cobblestone appearance of the chin and to fade the appearance of marionette, nasolabial and bunny lines.

Botox can also be used for the treatment of hyperhidrosis (excessive sweating) and can even be added to mesotherapy cocktails to reduce the appearance of wide pores and reduce oily skin.

Hold on, though, the list isn't finished – Botox can also be used for the scalp, which you may have read in disbelief in a magazine, but yes, it is possible.

With a skilful, knowledgeable practitioner, you can have Botox, look fab, and no one will know your secret.

Mesotherapy

As we age, our skin gets thinner and more dehydrated. The amount of collagen and elastin in the tissue is slowly depleted and wrinkles appear on the face. Low-viscosity hyaluronic acid can be applied as a support to the withered skin.

What Is Mesotherapy?

This treatment is designed to improve skin quality. Modern meso products are based on light-cohesivity hyaluronic acid and may also have a combination of vitamins, minerals, antioxidants and amino acids that is injected into the dermis of your skin.

The product is injected or applied into your skin with the help of a meso gun, small fine needles, or a medical microneedling device. A topical anaesthetic can be applied, but if a meso gun is used, the procedure is usually pain-free and does not require any kind of anaesthetic.

How Many Treatments Will I Need?

Depending on your skin condition, between three to six sessions will be recommended. A session can be done every two to four weeks.

Topical Treatments

If you are not a fan of the needles but still want to have flawless and youthful skin, we have some effective treatment options for you.

Topical treatments can be effectively administered by experienced and qualified therapists or your medical aesthetic practitioner.

Skin Peels

Chemical peels have a variety of strengths, so they can be used to target different skin conditions. Whether you would like to rejuvenate your skin and get a healthy, glowing complexion or target acne, scarring or pigmentation, this could be a great treatment for you! This is a treatment that has been around for many decades and can help to slow down the ageing process. Chemical peels work by deeply exfoliating the surface layers of the skin, forcing your body to quickly replenish it with new cells. They also stimulate the skin's natural collagen production to help target the appearance of fine lines and wrinkles. When peels are performed regularly, the skin gets used to this process and begins to rejuvenate itself like younger skin. To be sure that the body doesn't react to this exfoliation as it would to trauma, which can lead to pigmentation changes, exfoliation must be introduced gradually, giving the skin time to adjust.

What Happens During the Procedure?

Your therapist will prepare your face with a thorough cleanse. The chemical peel will be then applied. You will feel a mild to moderate tingling sensation depending on the strength of the peel. Your therapist will monitor your comfort level and adjust the time to your individual needs. Your face will be then cleansed, moisturised, and protected with SPF. Immediately after your peel, you might experience some redness and your face may feel a bit warm and tight.

What Results Can You Expect?

Mild peels are primarily used to freshen the skin and give you a nice glowing look. Stronger peels will improve the texture of your skin and smooth the surface, which will, in turn, reduce any scarring or pigmentation. To retain the results, you will need to repeat your treatment periodically – every few weeks for mild ones and perhaps every six months for stronger peels.

There are many different peels available – the list of manufacturers and distributors are endless – but most are based on essential acids, and each acid is specific to a certain skin condition. Some example acids are: salicylic, glycolic, mandelic, pyruvic, Jessner, lactic. These peels can be applied by a therapist. Strong peels that can penetrate into the deeper layers of our skin can only be administered by medical practitioners, such as TCA and Phenol peels.

Radiofrequency

As we age, collagen production slows down, skin loses its elasticity, and the contours of the face and body appear less defined. Normal changes in skin that come as we age include more visible wrinkles and sagging skin, uneven texture, dryness, and thinning of the superficial layer of the skin. Radiofrequency therapy can smooth, tighten, and contour skin for an overall younger-looking appearance. Radiofrequency has been described as a "non-surgical facelift" and is recognised for its body skin-tightening results. It is a non-invasive procedure that helps tighten and contour your skin. Treatment may be done in a single session or multiple sessions, depending on what machine the clinic is using.

The big advantage of radiofrequency is that it doesn't involve surgery or injections and no recovery time at all. Instead, it stimulates your body's natural renewal of collagen, which creates subtle, natural-looking results. Radiofrequency is an effective treatment for skin tightening on the face, neck, and décolletage, as well as the body. The treatment is an effective solution for sagging skin, loose jowls or lack of definition in the jawline, sagging skin under the chin and wrinkles and fine lines around the mouth and forehead. Radiofrequency works on all skin types on and off the face. It produces subtle and gradual results, resulting in smooth, sleek skin and an overall younger-looking appearance.

How Does It Work?

The treatment uses heat from the radiofrequency to target the cells within the skin to prompt them to produce more collagen. It causes an immediate tightening as excess water from the cells are released, but over the next few months after the treatment, the micro-damage it has caused prompts the cells to produce more collagen. This helps create smoother skin after treatment and the results continue to improve over time.

Who Is Suitable for Radiofrequency Treatment?

As long as you are generally healthy and don't have any skin diseases or infections in the area you wish to treat, there are few medical reasons why you should not have radiofrequency, making it a perfect treatment for so many people. However, it is particularly suitable for those who suffer from:

- Skin with soft tissue laxity, where the skin begins to feel and look less firm
- Sagging skin
- Skin with fine lines and wrinkles
- Skin that is generally showing signs of ageing

What Is the Treatment Like?

Your therapist will select a suitable handpiece and move it across your skin in a uniform pattern, delivering short pulses of energy to stimulate the skin. Some radiofrequency systems incorporate vibration into the face and body treatments, which has been shown to provide patient comfort. You'll feel a brief heating sensation when the treatment device's tip touches your skin, followed by a cooling sensation to help protect your skin and minimise any discomfort. It is a quick and easy treatment. It takes around thirty to ninety minutes, depending on the size of the area being treated.

LED Mask

This treatment uses LED (light-emitting diode) light therapy for skin rejuvenation and skin healing. LED light came into use when developments made by NASA researchers showed that certain frequencies of light significantly increased new tissue growth and stimulated collagen. Some scientific studies have concluded that skin cells can repair themselves up to twice as fast when subject to particular wavelengths of light. Quite simply, the treatment causes your skin to rejuvenate and heal faster. An LED face mask is a modern way to treat skin with light therapy. It works by exposing light to the skin surface and accelerating the cells' biochemical circulation.

LED light therapy is a non-invasive treatment that uses different wavelengths to rejuvenate and heal the skin. The breakthrough technology doesn't use any heat or invasive procedures but triggers the body to convert light energy into cell energy. The light stimulates the fibroblasts, which produce collagen and slow down the enzymes that break down collagen. Finally, it speeds up cell production, making skin regenerate faster for a fresher-looking complexion. The LED mask has a different setting to target different depths of the skin. Our experienced therapist will choose the appropriate wavelength for your skin type to achieve the best possible results. Results and treatment frequencies of the LED therapy can vary depending on your skin type and concerns. The treatment is pain-free and the visible effects are immediate. The LED face mask sits on the face with openings for the eyes, nose, and mouth to ensure complete coverage of the face.

Treatments are suitable for nearly all skin types. LED therapy can be used to treat:

- Sun-damaged skin
- Skin pigmentation
- Fine lines and wrinkles

- Acne and problem skin
- Sensitive and inflamed skin

The practitioner will prepare the area to be treated with a thorough cleanse. The mask will be placed on your face and switched on. You will feel like the sun is shining on your face and it should be relaxing. Treatment takes around twenty minutes. Treatment times are short, and the visible effects are, in most cases, immediate. The process instantly revives a tired and dull complexion. After just one treatment, skin is visibly brighter, smooth and radiant, while redness and irritation are calmed. There is no recovery time following an LED treatment and no specific aftercare.

Medical Microneedling

As we age and battle skin conditions, the natural architecture of our skin deteriorates, which leads to fine lines, wrinkles, large pores and uneven skin texture. Collagen induction therapy, also known as microneedling, is a great way to address these signs of ageing at the cellular level. Medical microneedling is a very effective treatment for acne scarring too. Microneedling comfortably creates thousands of micro-injuries in the skin to trigger the body's natural wound-healing process. This results in skin remodelling, including the formation of collagen and elastin, the two proteins predominantly responsible for the structure of the skin. The outcome is beautiful, youthful-looking skin.

Microneedling is a safe treatment. The results are gradual, with some visible results seen within the first several days. The recommendation is to have a minimum of three treatments to maximise results, depending on the patient's goal. This might be to reduce the signs of ageing or acne scarring.

What Happens During the Procedure?

Your therapist will cleanse your skin ready for the microneedling and apply a topical anaesthetic so the treatment won't be uncomfortable. She will then use the tool over your skin in controlled motions, which will puncture your skin in columns of around 0.5–2mm in depth, depending on your skin needs. Depending on the area being treated and the depth of the needle, your side effects may range from mild to more moderate. They include:

- Redness
- Sore skin
- Warm/tight skin
- Sensitive skin

Aftercare

You may look and feel as though you have sunburn, so we recommend:

- A thorough handwashing regime before touching the area
- Avoiding make-up for at least twenty-four hours
- Avoiding the sun on the area while it heals
- Avoiding fake tan products before and after your procedure

After the procedure, your skin starts to regenerate and repair itself below the surface. New collagen and skin cells are formed and blood to the area is increased, and within around four weeks, you'll be able to see the first stage of results. Over the months that follow, your skin will constantly improve to give you a natural and long-lasting result. Procedures can be done every four to six weeks.

Medical-Grade Facials

Many of us have experienced, in spas and salons, a relaxing, cleansing, exfoliating or massaging type of facial, with fragranced essential oils and feel-good products. From a clinical point of view, they probably only hydrate your skin, as well as offer certain antioxidants and exfoliation of dead skin cells. The aim of clinical facials is to address skin concerns, improve skin health and prevent significant skin issues. Acne can be helped; rosacea can be improved; lines and wrinkles can be softened; scarring corrected; skin can be tightened; ageing can be slowed!

Leading technologies are often used, such as radiofrequency, LED, vacuum or cavitation. You'll see medical-grade products on the practitioner's trolley rather than cosmetic products. You may also see needling devices used to deliver products to the deeper layers of the skin and optimise the treatment process as well as to regenerate tissue and stimulate collagen and elastin. Or chemical peels with the same purpose. These treatments will tackle the underlying issues your skin is facing, backed by clinical studies and from reputable medical cosmeceutical brands.

What Can You Expect from a Medical-Grade Facial?

Proper skincare analysis. A medical aesthetician will properly analyse your skin and discuss with you their recommendations for the best treatment options. Sometimes, it takes just the right skincare analysis and consultation of your overall wellness to give you the answers you're seeking.

Customised Treatment Plan

Now that you and your skincare professional are on the same page, it's time for a customised treatment plan. This typically starts with a facial that's tailored to your unique skin (and may include a combination of certain enzymes, peptides and/or added services like LED light therapy, microneedling, or chemical peel to targeted issues). After the procedure is completed, it is important that you follow the post-procedure protocol outlined by your skincare professional. This is especially important if your medical facial incorporates treatments that increase your skin's sensitivity to UV light.

Benefits of Medical-Grade Facials

- Results-driven
- Treats skin challenges like rosacea, acne, scarring, fine lines, wrinkles, dehydrated skin, sun damage, pigmentation
- Use of medical-grade ingredients and equipment to treat skin health effectively
- Deep cleansing without disrupting the natural barrier function of your skin
- Extraction of blackheads, whiteheads, and congested pores
- Exfoliation with the use of chemical peels, enzymes, and/or microdermabrasion, which are effective for skin renewal and better product absorption
- Hydration is crucial to the medical-grade facial and will protect your skin and allow for healthy progress

Utilise the aftercare instructions and home care products (that you can buy in-salon) to continue your customised skincare regimen. Keep in mind, you may need several customised treatments or to maintain a healthy facial schedule to see better results and reveal that glow.

Your Age-Appropriate Treatment Plan

While there is no one correct answer at what age we should start receiving treatments, there is one clear piece of advice: you should always look after your skin and get expert advice on what options are available and suitable for you.

The fact is that at the age of twenty-five, our body stops producing collagen, and so the ageing process begins. Luckily for us, it is a slow process and we have some time to make up our minds and decide how we want to age.

Our personal opinion, as women and as experts in the anti-ageing medical field, is that, if you are concerned about how you age, ask for advice and get help from an expert practitioner. Don't leave it until the problems become more severe.

Treatment Plan

And this is our gift to you, lovely reader: an age-appropriate treatment plan. In this section, we list the most common problems that we've seen in the clinic, aiming the guide at different age groups and detailing the most appropriate treatment solutions for them.

Twenties

Problem	Solution
Acne and breakouts	At home: good skincare routine, prescriptive retinol, review your diet. In clinic: LED light, extraction or deep-cleansing facial, microdermabrasion, skin peels (salicylic, mandelic, TCA).
Pigmentation	At home: prescriptive skincare, retinols, hydroquinone, SPF. In clinic: vitamin A & C ionophoresis facials, skin peels (Jessner, TCA), microdermabrasion.
Dull, dry skin	At home: good skincare routine (minimal requirements: cleanser, hydrate, protect). In clinic: hydrating facials, mandelic skin peel, mesotherapy with hyaluronic acid.
Open pores	At home: prescriptive skincare, acid-based cleanser and retinol can be quite effective. In clinic: extraction or deep-cleansing facial, microdermabrasion, medical microneedling, skin peels.

Rosacea	At home: medical-grade prescriptive skincare. In clinic: anti-inflammatory facial, skin peels, LED light.
Fine lines	At home: prescriptive skincare. In clinic: skin peels, mesotherapy, microneedling.
Dynamic lines	At home: prescriptive skincare. In clinic: anti-wrinkle injection, mesotherapy.
Acne scarring	At home: prescriptive skincare. In clinic: medical microneedling, bioremodelling with hyaluronic acid.
Structural hereditary facial problems such as lack of facial structure, cheekbones, chin, jawline area, gummy smile, facial asymmetries	In clinic: volumising fillers, botulinum toxin injections, other options can be considered.

Thirties

Problem	Solution
Adult acne	At home: good skincare routine, prescriptive retinol, review your diet. In clinic: LED light, extraction or deep-cleansing facial, microdermabrasion, skin peels.
Pigmentation	At home: prescriptive skincare, retinols, hydroquinone, SPF. In clinic: vitamin A & C ionophoresis facials, skin peels (Jessner, TCA), microdermabrasion.
Dull, dry skin	At home: skincare routine. In clinic: hydrating facials, mandelic skin peel, mesotherapy with HA.
Open pores	At home: prescriptive skincare. In clinic: extraction or deep-cleansing facial, microdermabrasion, medical microneedling, skin peels.
Rosacea	At home: prescriptive skincare. In clinic: anti-inflammatory facial, skin peels.
Fine lines	At home: prescriptive skincare. In clinic: skin peels, mesotherapy, microneedling.

Dynamic lines	At home: prescriptive skincare. In clinic: anti-wrinkle injection, mesotherapy.
Acne scarring	At home: prescriptive skincare. In clinic: medical microneedling, bioremodelling, hyaluronic acid.
Structural hereditary facial problems such as lack of facial structure, cheekbones, chin, jawline area, gummy smile, facial asymmetries	In clinic: volumising fillers, botulinum toxin injections.
Dark circles under the eyes and eye bags	In clinic: medical-grade skincare, carboxytherapy, tear trough filler.
Early appearance of jowls, deep nasolabial and marionette lines	In clinic: dermal fillers in the midface area (cheeks).
First changes in the neck area	In clinic: skin boosters, anti-wrinkle (Nefertiti) neck lift, radiofrequency.

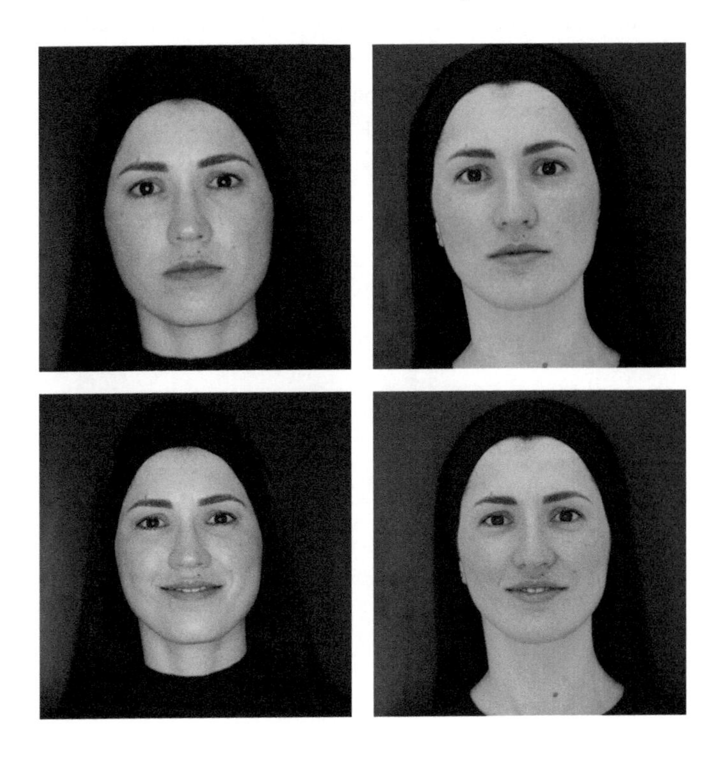

Prevention is better than cure and during your thirties is the perfect time to start thinking about how you would like to age.

There are a range of options available for you at this early stage of ageing, from skincare, peels and facials to injectable treatments.

Often, a busy lifestyle and family life affects patients' decisions. Therefore, injectable treatment may be at the top of the list for the simple reason that they work and they last, especially while we still have good collagen and volume of our own.

This beautiful patient was treated using a minimal amount of Hyaluronic acid filler, yet we achieved an incredible improvement.

Beautification and a balancing facial proportion, making the patient look fresh and more feminine.

Forties

Problem	Solution
Adult acne	At home: good skincare routine, prescriptive retinol, review your diet. In clinic: LED light, extraction or deep-cleansing facial, microdermabrasion, skin peels.
Pigmentation	At home: prescriptive skincare, retinols, hydroquinone, SPF. In clinic: vitamin A & C ionophoresis facials, skin peels (Jessner, TCA), microdermabrasion.
Dull, dry skin	At home: skincare routine. In clinic: hydrating facials, mandelic skin peel, mesotherapy with HA.
Open pores	At home: prescriptive skincare. In clinic: extraction or deep-cleansing facial, microdermabrasion, medical microneedling, skin peels.
Rosacea	At home: prescriptive skincare. In clinic: anti-inflammatory facial, skin peels.
Fine lines	At home: prescriptive skincare. In clinic: skin peels, mesotherapy, microneedling.

Dynamic lines	At home: prescriptive skincare. In clinic: anti-wrinkle injection, mesotherapy.
Acne scarring	At home: prescriptive skincare. In clinic: medical microneedling, biomodelling, hyaluronic acid.
Structural hereditary facial problems such as lack of facial structure, cheekbones, chin, jawline area, gummy smile, facial asymmetries	In clinic: volumising fillers, botulinum toxin injections.
Dark circles under the eyes and eye bags	In clinic: medical-grade skincare, carboxytherapy, tear trough filler.
Appearance of jowls, deep nasolabial and marionette lines	In clinic: dermal filler (liquid facelift), collagen-stimulating injections, PDO threads, radiofrequency.
Ageing of the neck area	In clinic: skin boosters, anti-wrinkle (Nefertiti) neck lift, radiofrequency.

Attractive at Forty

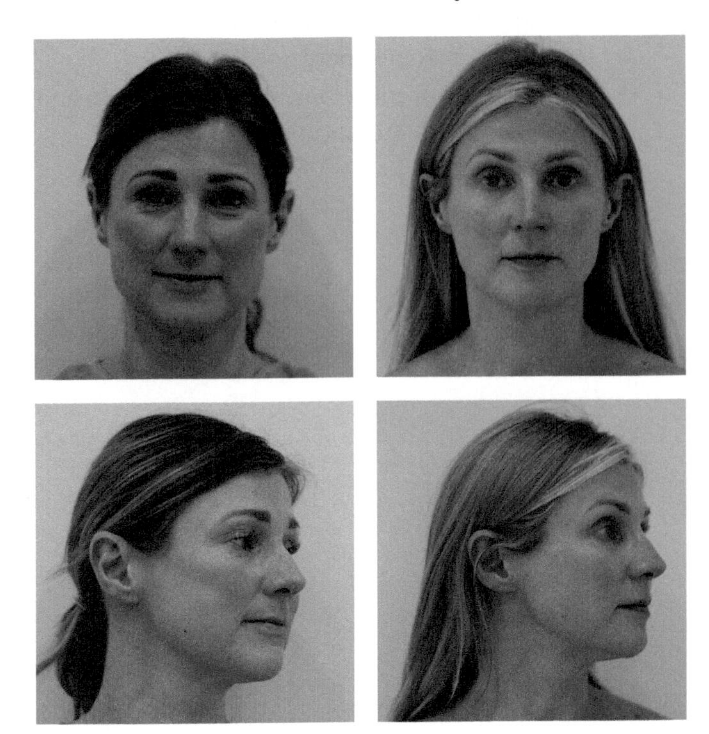

Forty is a big milestone in the modern world when we can call ourselves a fully grown-up person. But from a biological point of view, we already have a decade of ageing behind us.

Very often, patients come to our clinic as they see noticeable changes in their forties. This is the most common age to start looking at how to look a little fresher and how to reverse the signs of the very annoying ageing process.

In the case of our patient Karen, we applied a multi-treatment approach:

- PDO thread lift
- Beautification treatment with dermal fillers: temples, tear trough, nose and lips
- Muscle relaxant injections to the upper face and masseter muscle (mastication muscle)

Fifties

Problem	Solution
Pigmentation	At home: prescriptive skincare, retinols, hydroquinone, SPF. In clinic: vitamin A & C ionophoresis facials, skin peels (Jessner, TCA), microdermabrasion.
Dull, dry skin	At home: skincare routine. In clinic: hydrating facials, mandelic skin peel, mesotherapy with HA.
Open pores	At home: prescriptive skincare. In clinic: extraction or deep-cleansing facial, microdermabrasion, medical microneedling, skin peels.
Rosacea	At home: prescriptive skincare. In clinic: anti-inflammatory facial, skin peels.
Fine lines	At home: prescriptive skincare. In clinic: skin peels, mesotherapy, microneedling.
Dynamic lines	In clinic: anti-wrinkle injection, mesotherapy.

Acne scarring	At home: prescriptive skincare. In clinic: medical microneedling, biomodelling, hyaluronic acid.
Structural hereditary facial problems such as lack of facial structure, cheekbones, chin, jawline area, gummy smile, facial asymmetries	In clinic: volumising fillers, botulinum toxin injections.
Dark circles under the eyes and eye bags	In clinic: medical-grade skincare, carboxytherapy, tear trough filler.
Appearance of jowls, deep nasolabial and marionette lines, sagginess	In clinic: dermal filler (liquid facelift), PDO threads.
Ageing of the neck area	In clinic: skin boosters, anti-wrinkle (Nefertiti) neck lift.
Skin elastosis	In clinic: medical-grade skincare, lifting and skin remodelling peels, mesotherapy, collagen-stimulating injections.
Upper eyelid ptosis	In clinic: non-surgical blepharoplasty, surgical advice.

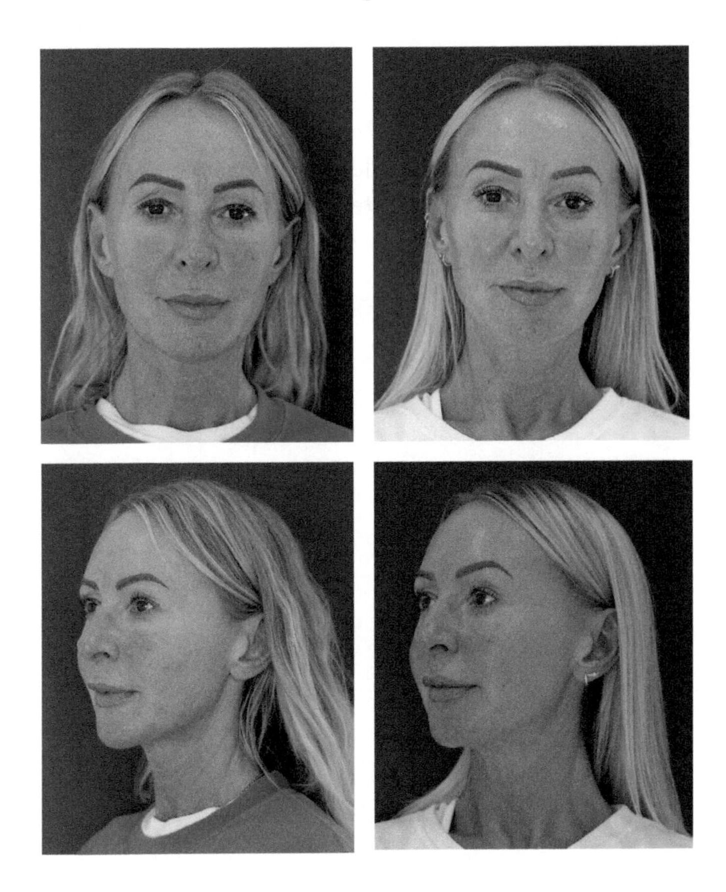

Botox and dermal fillers are not the answer for all our patients. We have never applied a one-size-fits-all approach in our practice. The foremost priority is working together with patients to achieve their goals within their comfort zone.

The case of our patient Lisa is a perfect example of how a small amount of dermal fillers, in combination with injectable skin boosters, can make a big difference.

Fresh, flawless skin, looking less tired, looking more youthful, those are the comments that come to mind when we look at these pictures.

Provided treatment:

- Temple and cheek filler with total volume 3ml
- Course of skin booster Teoxane Redensity 1 and RH 1

Sixties

Problem	Solution
Adult acne	At home: good skincare routine, prescriptive retinol, review your diet. In clinic: LED light, extraction or deep-cleansing facial, microdermabrasion, skin peels.
Pigmentation	At home: prescriptive skincare, retinols, hydroquinone, SPF. In clinic: vitamin A & C ionophoresis facials, skin peels (Jessner, TCA), microdermabrasion.
Dull, dry skin	At home: skincare routine. In clinic: hydrating facials, mandelic skin peel, mesotherapy with HA.
Open pores	At home: prescriptive skincare. In clinic: extraction or deep-cleansing facial, microdermabrasion, medical microneedling, skin peels.
Rosacea	At home: prescriptive skincare. In clinic: anti-inflammatory facial, skin peels.
Fine lines	At home: prescriptive skincare In clinic: skin peels, mesotherapy, microneedling.

Dynamic lines	At home: prescriptive skincare. In clinic: anti-wrinkle injection, mesotherapy.
Acne scarring	At home: prescriptive skincare. In clinic: medical microneedling, bioremodelling, hyaluronic acid.
Structural hereditary facial problems such as lack of facial structure, cheekbones, chin, jawline area, gummy smile, facial asymmetries	In clinic: volumising fillers, botulinum toxin injections.
Dark circles under the eyes and eye bags	In clinic: medical-grade skincare, carboxytherapy, tear trough filler.
Appearance of jowls, deep nasolabial and marionette lines, sagginess	In clinic: dermal filler (liquid facelift), PDO threads.
Ageing of the neck area	In clinic: skin boosters, biorevitalisers, anti-wrinkle (Nefertiti) neck lift, liquid neck lift with filler, fractional needling, PDO neck lift.

Skin elastosis	In clinic: medical-grade skincare, lifting and skin remodelling peels, mesotherapy, collagen-stimulating injections.
Upper eyelid ptosis	In clinic: non-surgical blepharoplasty, surgical blepharoplasty.

Fabulous at Sixty

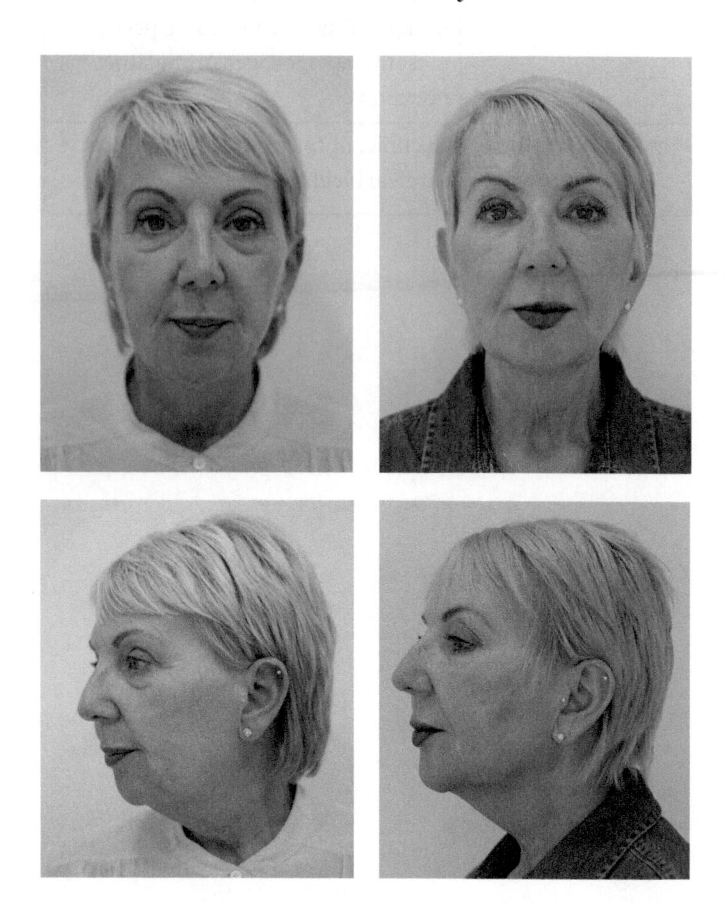

Some people think about retirement at sixty when others are ready to conquer the world. Which type are you? Well, let us tell you that we treat so many ladies of this age group who look absolutely fabulous.

Yes, the treatment needs may be higher and we need to see you more often, but the impact treatment has on your confidence and day-to-day life is absolutely incredible.

Jean says, 'It makes me smile when people question my age.'

Dermal fillers, PDO and Botox are your best friends at this stage.

These beautiful results were achieved using 10ml (equivalent to a teaspoon) of HA fillers Maili.

- Treated areas:
- Temple
- Cheeks
- Chin
- Jawline
- Nasolabial folds
- Tear trough

Seventies and Eighties

Problem	Solution
Pigmentation	At home: skincare retinols, hydroquinone, SPF. In clinic: vitamin A & C ionophoresis facials, skin peels, microdermabrasion.
Dull, dry skin	At home: skincare routine. In clinic: hydrating facials, mandelic skin peel, mesotherapy with HA.
Open pores	At home: prescriptive skincare. In clinic: extraction or deep-cleansing facial, microdermabrasion, medical microneedling, skin peels.
Rosacea	At home: prescriptive skincare. In clinic: anti-inflammatory facial, skin peels.
Fine lines	At home: prescriptive skincare. In clinic: skin peels, mesotherapy, microneedling.
Dynamic lines	At home: prescriptive skincare. In clinic: anti-wrinkle injection, mesotherapy.

Structural hereditary facial problems such as lack of facial structure, cheekbones, chin, jawline area, gummy smile, facial asymmetries	In clinic: volumising fillers, botulinum toxin injections.
Dark circles under the eyes and eye bags	In clinic: medical-grade skincare, carboxytherapy, tear trough filler.
Appearance of jowls, deep nasolabial and marionette lines, sagginess	In clinic: dermal filler (liquid facelift), PDO threads.
Ageing of the neck area	In clinic: skin boosters, anti-wrinkle (Nefertiti) neck lift.
Skin elastosis	In clinic: medical-grade skincare, lifting and skin remodelling peels, mesotherapy, collagen-stimulating injections.
Upper eyelid ptosis	In clinic: non-surgical blepharoplasty, surgical blepharoplasty.
Skeletal changes due to bone resorption	In clinic: dermal fillers, collagen-stimulating injections, thread lifts, combination of multiple therapies.

Seventy Is the New Forty and Eighty the New Fifty – Why Can't It Be This Way?

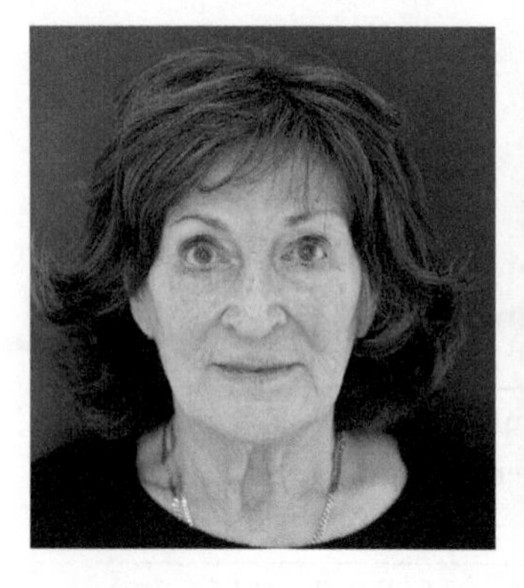

We are only as old as we feel.

We are inspired by our beautiful patients who believe that it's never too old to be beautiful, have some self-care and self-love.

Because you're worth it.

This subtle yet noticeable transformation was achieved with the following treatment plan:

- Anti-wrinkle injection to the upper face
- Perioral rejuvenation with hyaluronic-acid-based filler Maili
- Mid-face volumisation with hyaluronic-acid-based filler Maili

Disclaimer: patients gave us full permission to share their photos and treatment.

Chapter Five

Customers' Stories

Andrea

Firstly, could you tell us a little about your background?
I'm fifty-two, upped sticks and left my husband and home town at forty-five with just a suitcase (because I took the sports car, darlings, and that's all I could fit in!) and ended up in Nottingham, purely because that's where I worked. I found out I'd gone through the menopause in my early forties and had to seek a private GP as my doctor wouldn't give me oestrogen. Ladies, it's your choice and your body;

we're living longer – we don't have to settle for fatigue. So with the help of a colleague, I wrote a menopause awareness site at work to help and support others. Which I guess is why I'm here. We all need to support each other, and we all need to have the right information to make our own informed choices about what's right for us. We don't have to be like our mums and nans and suffer in silence; we can be the best that we can be!

When/why did you first consider looking for advice on aesthetic or skin treatments?

I was in my early fifties and found out that I'd gone through the menopause over five years ago! Great, very few symptoms, but the lack of collagen and oestrogen showed in my skin. Besides, it was time to look after myself. After all, wasn't everyone having a little Botox here and there? Admittedly, some were more successful than others, but whilst I had done OK ageing wise, my overexpressive face showed I didn't suffer fools. And, let's face it, after the menopause, none of us suffer fools that lightly. It was time to take action!

How long did it take you between considering treatment and booking a consultation?

I didn't want to be frozen; I wanted to be me but better. I didn't want it to be openly noticeable. So I asked friends, including those who had been "frozen". After all, I didn't want to go to the same place as them and end up looking like them. I also asked for recommendations from friends who looked great. I went for consultations and if I didn't feel comfortable or was being "upsold", I didn't proceed. Eventually, I knew I'd found my consultant when she had the face and skin that I envied. All in all, it took over three months.

How did you research before calling to book?
Lots of recommendations from friends, lots of visits. I had to feel comfortable. Be brave enough to say no. It was my money and my face.

What factors were important to you when choosing your clinic?
No pushy upsells, a comfortable environment, someone who understood what I wanted, someone who explained clearly the pre-care and aftercare, and told me what they could and couldn't do for me.

Were you worried about having treatments? If so, why?
We've all seen the Bride of Wildenstein and don't want to go down that path! I didn't want people asking if I'd had treatment; I wanted to be able to tell them if I wanted to.

Would it have been useful to read a book about other people's experiences? If so, why?
Yes, especially if it was people local to me. The first time I had Botox around my eyes, it freaked me out when it kicked in as I couldn't lift my eyelids to apply eye make-up. I thought I'd had a stroke! Now I know more about it, I can ask for that area to be avoided. I still want to look like me, just a better me.

When you decided to go ahead, how did the treatment make you feel?
It felt like an investment. I'd done something purely for me, something that (hopefully) no one would know about unless I chose to tell them, but they'd just think, *oh, she's looking well.*

Would you continue to have the treatment and would you recommend it to other women?
Absolutely, I've now had a little filler around the marionette lines. Again, just a small amount. If it bothers you, and you can afford it, get it sorted. It's not for everyone and I would never "force" anyone, but bear in mind when you have had "tweakments", you do go around judging people. My friend commented that I was listening intently to her; I was actually looking at her face, thinking, *you look angry when you talk and just a little bit of Botox would sort that out...* Sshhh, don't tell her – I was listening, honestly!

Karen

I am a forty-five-year-old housewife with a busy and colourful home life. When I turned forty, I really didn't know what all the fuss was about. I felt amazing and really had no concerns about ageing. However, at forty-two, I really noticed a difference in my appearance. I started noticing lines and wrinkles, which I took in my stride and accepted as part of the ageing process. But what really bothered me was the obvious effects of gravity, how things were moving south! I felt I looked tired and droopy and needed a lift. The woman I went to for my regular facials had recently been to Angels Twelve and had the thread facelift. She was delighted with the results, and I thought she looked great, so I booked an appointment.

Olha discussed the various options available to me and suggested areas I should have treated that I had never thought of. This was the whole face approach; rather than just focusing on one area, you make subtle changes to improve your overall appearance. I made the appointment and waited about three weeks for the day to arrive. I was nervous as I'd not had anything like this before, and I had decided to go for several procedures all at once. However, having a first-hand testimonial did help reassure me.

The experience on the day was very positive. The clinic was very clean, and the staff were all very friendly and professional. I was very pleased with the initial results. Even though I was bruised and swollen, I could see I had achieved the results I was looking for. The aftercare was very good, with phone calls to check in with me and follow-up consultations. I had started my aesthetics journey!

Since then, I've had various treatments recommended by Olha. I would definitely recommend the treatments I have had to other women who are considering this. The confidence it has given me is great. I am so happy with my appearance now, and it's not just about anti-ageing. I have rectified areas of my face that I have never been happy with, areas such as my nose and jaw. Overall, my experience has been very positive. I feel that for the rest of my life, I'll continue having a variety of treatments.

Olivia

I decided to invest in my skin journey after going on an overall health kick. I felt like I was healthy and fit, yet my skin didn't show that. I wanted that "glow". I rarely wear make-up and it was my goal to have skin that I felt didn't need make-up. My pores were large, my skin uneven and dry. I did some research, looking specifically for the Obagi skin range after seeing so many good results with their products. I had a thorough consultation with Dr Olha and booked my first appointment as soon as possible. I was so excited to start the process towards healthier skin and to have a good skin regime that works.

I started with a deep-cleansing facial and immediately saw clearer results and was sent home with a few select products that I could incorporate into my busy morning routine with two babies. I was so happy to have a low-maintenance skin routine that I could finally stick to and have since built upon, only with advice from the Angels Twelve practitioners.

Alongside my at-home skincare, I started a series of microneedling and mild abrasive peels. From my first treatment, I was hooked! It was completely painless, which I was a little surprised by, and the process has given me the results I had always been wanting.

At just twenty-six years old, I have been told time and time again that the younger you start, the better your results in the future, which has always stuck with me. To me, my skin is the best investment I could make for myself now and for my future self. I am so pleased to have finally found a clinic that understands my skin so in-depth that I can now confidently wear a fresh face every day. I can honestly say I won't touch my skin without advice from Dr Olha or Johanna (therapist who works at Angels Twelve clinic). I finally have that "glow" I was searching for!

My top tip for anyone starting their own skin journey would be, always have your next appointment booked before you leave.

Rachel

Could you tell us a little about your background?
I am thirty-four years old and I live in the Peak District with my husband and two rescue dogs. I'm a chartered surveyor working in residential valuations. I love skiing, festivals, horse riding and scuba diving.

When/why did you first consider looking for advice on aesthetic or skin treatments?
I had been feeling for some time that I looked constantly tired. My under-eye area appeared quite hollow and dark, and tear trough filler was recommended to me (by a previous practitioner). Once I had the idea in my head, I convinced myself it was definitely the solution to my problems, despite very little research. I had no idea of the complexities of this particular area before deciding to go ahead. I had the tear trough filler carried out by the previous practitioner, but unfortunately, the results were not what I expected at all. After allowing time for them to settle down, my eye bags remained puffy and raised, with a slightly blue tinge, and one was fuller than the other. Whilst maybe not so obvious to others, it looked truly terrible to me in certain lights. I felt ten years older and very self-conscious. I invested in expensive concealer, which achieved nothing, so I reverted to wearing sunglasses when out.

How long did it take you between considering treatment and booking a consultation?
It took a good five months before I booked a consultation. This was partly due to lockdown and the fact I could mostly hibernate at home without seeing too many people.

I was also nervous about the dissolving procedure and potentially ending up in a worse position than I was then. And finally, I was hoping it would begin to break down on its own as I neared the six-month point. However, I then found out through some online research that filler can last much longer in this area which coincided with the main catalyst for my decision: the pubs opened.

How did you research before calling to book?
I used Google to research the procedure and potential clinics as well as read client reviews on various platforms. What I found very frustrating was the lack of real-life experiences and photos documented online as opposed to the generic descriptions on most websites. I wanted to hear and see someone who had been through what I had and have the reassurance of knowing they had come out the other side unscathed.

What factors were important to you when choosing your clinic?
I was looking for clinics within a reasonable distance to me and ones that appeared professional from their marketing and reviews. But most importantly, I wanted a very experienced practitioner who would consider the best options for me, especially given my previous experience and the delicate area of treatment. During this research process, Dr Olha was highly recommended to me, for which I am ever so grateful.

Were you worried about having treatments? If so, why?
I was definitely worried about the procedure, but more in respect to how I would look afterwards – was I jumping out of the frying pan into the fire? The original tear trough

procedure had not been too painful, but would dissolving be any different? Again, this was something I hadn't been able to establish from my research, so that was a bit of an unknown until I had my consultation. As it turned out, I had nothing to worry about.

Would it have been useful to read a book about other people's experiences? If so, why?
Having a resource like that from a reputable source would be worth its weight in gold. I imagine it would help many others in the same position as me, needing to get my filler dissolved. And whilst online research can be handy, you never really know how trustworthy it is. Being able to see photographs of cases would also be immensely useful in the decision-making process.

When you decided to go ahead, how did the treatment make you feel?
The filler began to dissolve during the treatment, which was not painful at all, and when I looked in the mirror after half an hour, I was absolutely delighted. For the first time in five months, it was my own face looking back at me and that was such a relief. Dr Olha then showed me my before and after photos, and seeing them side by side was fascinating. To others, perhaps only a slight difference was noticeable, but to me, it was massive. There was hardly any bruising as a result of the treatment. In fact, you could barely tell I had had any procedure at all.

Would you continue to have the treatment and would you recommend it to other women?
Hopefully, I will never have to have this particular procedure again, but if someone was unhappy with

their results, I would recommend considering having it dissolved, in the hands of an experienced professional, of course. I learnt my lesson the first time around, so when it came to this procedure, only the best would do! And that goes for all future treatments too.

Rebecca

Could you tell us a little about your background?
My name is Rebecca Richards and I am nearly forty-two years old. I'm originally from Derby, now living in Nottingham. When I was younger, I was bullied a lot for the way I looked. My teeth were twisted; I had my dad's big bushy eyebrows; and I was short, so I was an easy target. Because of this, I left school at fourteen with no exams or education, so growing up was difficult and I lacked confidence. I would look at other women and just wish I looked like them; I would try to think of ways to make myself look different with make-up, but it would never work. I would never smile, and I would keep my head down.

As I got older and had my children, I started to really look at myself and my life. I decided I needed to go to university and get myself an education, which I did. Along the way, I gained confidence within myself. Once I started to earn my own money, I came across Botox, and my journey began. I wouldn't say aesthetics is the sole reason why I'm happy, but it's certainly helped me with my confidence, and because of that, it's opened other doors for me. I'm now living comfortably. I work hard; I have two amazing children and a fiancé whom I'm marrying next year.

When/why did you first consider looking for advice on aesthetic or skin treatments?
I was twenty-nine years old when I first considered having Botox. I used to have this awful frown line between my eyes, and every morning I would wake up and constantly focus on it. Every time I walked past a mirror, it would be the first thing my eyes would divert to; it drove me mad.

How long did it take you between considering treatment and booking a consultation?
It took me six months. I was really worried about what it would feel like and if it would suit me. In the end, I just booked an appointment, as seeing the line far outweighed the worry of what Botox would feel like and would be worth it if it helped with the way I felt about myself.

How did you research before calling to book?
The very first time, I found a deal on Groupon and from there found a clinic locally to where I lived. This is something I would never recommend! From there, I attended two other clinics through advertisements and then a good friend of mine told me about Cosmetic Courses. Then, three or four years ago, through Cosmetic Courses, I met Olha.

What factors were important to you when choosing your clinic?
I wanted the person who was administering the aesthetics to be certified and be confident in what they were doing. It was important that the clinic was a sterile place and

that previous customers were happy with their results. It's important to have someone who will listen to what you want but who will also advise against procedures if you don't really need them. If you're someone like me who gets carried away, then it's important that you choose a good clinic that wants to help you look your best. It was unfortunate at the beginning of my aesthetics journey that I chose a bad clinic that made some errors on my face! I had a tear trough that left an awful lump under my eye and lip filler that left my lips slightly wonky in shape. Fortunately, I found Olha, who was able to correct these issues for me.

Were you worried about having treatments? If so, why?
I was worried that things might go wrong or that I might have a reaction. Hearing things in the media over the years and not understanding the treatments played a big factor in my worries. It's important to talk these through at the clinic. Yes, things did go wrong, which is why it's so important to find the right clinic and do your research.

Would it have been useful to read a book about other people's experiences? If so, why?
Yes, I think I would have researched a lot more, asked more questions and asked to see pictures of previous clients to see their results. It may have given me the confidence to say no and walk away when it felt like they were more interested in taking my money rather than enhancing my features.

When you decided to go ahead, how did the treatment make you feel?
Once I found the right place, the treatments have made

me feel *so* much more confident. I feel like my face is in proportion now and certain areas are highlighted that make me look and feel great. I love how Olha gives you a natural look.

Would you continue to have the treatment and would you recommend it to other women?
I will always continue to have treatments for as long as I can and yes, I would absolutely recommend them to other women. Some of my friends tell me "you should just be happy" and "just grow old gracefully!", but I'm happier now than I have ever been! If I had listened to these friends, then I wouldn't have the confidence and grace that I now have.

Sarah

At the age of about forty-five, I found myself being more critical of my appearance. I started noticing small details on my face, such as lines and wrinkles, that previously I never had. This, in turn, made me feel older, invisible, maybe even a little vulnerable, something that I had never associated with myself before. I spoke to friends who were about the same age, some of whom accepted what was happening to them, but others were thinking of turning to aesthetics to help turn back the clock.

Although I had always looked after my skin and invested in regular facials etc., the idea of aesthetics was quite daunting and filled me with dread and uncertainty, but something inside me wanted to know more. Although I am a qualified nurse, my knowledge of aesthetics was minimal, and to be perfectly honest, throughout this journey, I have been conflicted. Part of me was annoyed that my appearance was so important and I thought I should accept ageing gracefully as nature intended, but I do like to look my best to feel empowered and strong.

My first insight into aesthetics was by an invite to a Botox party. I didn't feel confident enough to have anything done at the time, but it did pique my interest, so I researched different treatments and aesthetic practitioners. There are definitely some horror stories out there that made me super cautious, but after a while, I came across Dr Olha. She was recommended to me by one of her previous clients. At that time, she did occasional clinics at a local beauticians that I visited, so I was able to talk to other ladies who had consulted her. After hearing their stories, I felt comfortable enough to arrange a consultation.

It was important to me to get across to Dr Olha that I just wanted to look fresher, less tired, stronger, and look the best I could without changing how I looked. I didn't want it to be obvious to friends and family that I had had anything done. Dr Olha got it completely, and from that day to now, I trust her opinion. She alleviated any fears I had about pain, side effects etc. I enjoy going to visit her at the clinic. The staff are friendly, professional and welcoming. The clinic environment is immaculate. There is never any time pressure and all the procedures are explained in a way that anyone can understand. Once I have had a treatment done, it makes me feel fabulous. It makes me want to get dressed up, put my make-up on and go out – it's marvellous.

My experience of aesthetics has been a positive one and I would encourage anyone interested to seek out Dr Olha. I will continue to see Dr Olha; I have complete faith in her. I know she will give me an honest opinion and support and guide me through any decisions I make about future aesthetic treatments.

Yana

Could you tell us a little about your background?
I work in the printing industry, where we print books, magazines, calendars and folders. Although our premises are really clean, I do feel that the dust particles were having an effect on my skin. I just wasn't happy with the way I looked. I decided I had to change, so I found Angels Twelve and it was a great choice.

When/why did you first consider looking for advice on aesthetic or skin treatments?
Around five years ago, I started thinking about having some treatments and started following the page at Angels Twelve. I was most interested to read the positive reviews from clients. After the first lockdown, I decided it was time to take some advice and booked an online consultation with Dr Olha by Zoom.

How long did it take you between considering treatment and booking a consultation?
I would say around two years because I wanted to see Dr

Olha at Angels Twelve, but I live an hour away from the clinic, so I had to consider the commitment and the time it would take me to visit. Had I really got that much time to spare for myself?

How did you research before calling to book?
I have known Dr Olha for around twelve years and the best possible way to decide was that my friend, whose skin looks amazing, recommended the clinic to me.

What factors were important when choosing your clinic?
Firstly, it was hygiene for me, along with friendly, professional, knowledgeable and helpful staff.

Were you worried about having treatments? If so, why?
No, I didn't feel worried because I knew that I'd chosen a very established clinic with positive reviews.

Would it have been useful to read a book about other people's experiences? If so, why?
For myself, I needed to see unedited photographs of before and after treatments.

When you decided to go ahead, how did the treatment make you feel?
Through consultation with Dr Olha, I decided to go for medical-grade skincare products to use at home, along with regular prescriptive facials. I can see the results and, honestly, it makes me feel so much happier.

Would you continue to have the treatment and would you recommend it to other women?
I will always carry on having my treatments; I can't wait

for them to come round. My skin is glowing, fresh and younger-looking. I don't wear heavy foundations anymore, which also helps to maintain healthy skin. I feel as though I'm achieving the best possible results for me and that's a fantastic feeling. I would recommend everyone to work with their doctor to improve their skin – it gives you so much confidence.

Vanessa

My focus on facial aesthetics began when I decided I wanted improvements on my teeth. I read articles about the different methods available. During this research, I noticed enhanced lips and how youthful they looked in comparison to my own skinny top lip which wasn't a good look. Often I would cringe at some of my photos and replenish my lipstick a little too often in the hope of disguising my thin smile.

When I reached fifty, I decided I wanted to make the best of my appearance and I accepted I probably needed some help. Olha was highly recommended to me and I was impressed by the brand of looking natural and rewinding several years. This was far more appealing than "fake", which I didn't want to look.

I had a consultation and was excited to get my first appointment for lip fillers. I guess I was a little nervous too as this was all new and daunting. What if I didn't like it? What if it hurt? I'm glad I ignored the "what ifs" because seeing the result after my first treatment, I felt overwhelmed and emotional. The improvement was dramatic and instant. It was fantastic. My skinny lips looked fuller. As promised, we started gradually and I achieved my desired look, which is natural.

Any reservations I'd initially had about aesthetics were gone. I had walked through a new door and stepped into a new journey and there is no going back for me. The transformation is life-changing. I feel confident, happy and no longer feel awkward about the ageing process. Olha and her team are there to work with my face not against it.

After achieving my perfect lips, I am currently going through an advanced teeth-whitening process and restructuring several teeth. Again, Olha is working with my teeth and improving only what's required.

In the future I may consider other treatments. I feel very lucky and happy to be on this journey.

Lisa

Could you tell us a little about your background?
I'm Lisa and I'm a forty-seven-year-old personal trainer and have been for over ten years. Because of my job, my health, fitness and well-being are all a large part of my life. I put a lot of time and effort into eating well and exercising daily, prepping foods and shopping for healthy alternatives, and wanted to do the same for my face and skin.

As I am a "little older" than most of the young personal trainers in the gym, I feel that it's time to spend more time on my face and body. At the end of the day, there is no point in having an amazing body with a saggy old face! So my mission now is to listen to Olha's fantastic advice, help and support to help me feel more facially confident when I am under constant scrutiny from clients and gym members. After all, they look at you first before signing up, so it's very important to me to look and feel my best.

When/why did you first consider looking for advice on aesthetic or skin treatments?
I first considered and took advice when I reached the age of forty.

How long did it take you between considering treatment and booking a consultation?
A few days as I knew I was ready.

How did you research before calling to book?
I researched by speaking to a lot of friends who had previously had treatments and procedures. I also reviewed the website and took my time looking at all of the individual procedures to see which ones were right for me.

What factors were important to you when choosing your clinic?
First and foremost the practitioner – I knew I had to have an experienced, knowledgeable and highly recommended practitioner with years of experience. I then had to factor in travel time – with me working split shifts, this was important to me also.

Were you worried about having treatments? If so, why?
Yes, I was a little anxious – with it being my face I wanted to get the right treatment for me, so it was important to get the right clinic.

Would it have been useful to read a book about other people's experiences? If so, why?
Yes, I do believe so, as I always read the reviews and love looking at before and after photos.

When you decided to go ahead, how did the treatment make you feel?
Wonderful – as soon as I've had the treatment I always feel so much better, more confident and happy.

Would you continue to have the treatment and would you recommend it to other women?
Absolutely, the difference that Olha has made to me is astonishing – I would highly recommend and always do so to my friends and colleagues.

Alexandra

Could you tell us a little about your background?
I am a single parent with two young boys and am a two-time breast cancer survivor. I have clocked up around ten surgeries over the past eight years. Everything from lumpectomies to mastectomies, lymph node removal to ovary and tube removal, as well as cosmetic procedures like fat grafting and nipple replacement, and not to mention the radiotherapy, ongoing hormone therapy and early menopause!

At not even forty, experiencing some of the side effects of the menopause (thinning and ageing of the skin) has left me feeling, and sometimes looking, rather tired and run-down. Sometimes it is nice to do something for me, just to make me feel better about myself – not for anyone else.

When/why did you first consider looking for advice on aesthetic or skin treatments?
I was about twenty-four I think, quite young, but I was working full-time in an office at a computer and I noticed

I was getting a really prominent frown line on my forehead from staring at the computer screen all day. People used to say I looked miserable (or had a resting bitch face).

How long did it take you between considering treatment and booking a consultation?
It was a quick decision for me. I knew exactly what I wanted doing (Botox) and had lots of friends at work who had already had it. I don't think it took me too long to make a decision.

How did you research before calling to book?
I don't remember doing any research, to be honest. I think I had heard a few others at work talking about it; I knew celebrities used it; I knew I was getting lines on my forehead that I didn't want; and my sister was interested too, so we just decided to go for it.

What factors were important to you when choosing your clinic?
I used another company (the SKIN clinic) back then... mainly because it was local and had a good reputation. It felt professional, hygienic, and very clinical, which made me feel safe and confident. However, I found it quite expensive and then decided to look around for other professionals who could administer Botox. After trialling various clinics and having various outcomes, I realised that this was not something I should be so blasé about. I wanted to use a professional that I could trust, not a back-street clinic or a retired nurse working from her living room. And that was when I was introduced through a friend to Dr Olha at her practice in West Bridgford.

I immediately felt that her professionalism and her expertise were superior to other professionals I had used previously. I found her advice really reassuring and she made me feel completely confident in her knowledge.

Were you worried about having treatments? If so, why?
Yes, I was nervous about new treatments like tear trough with canula because I had heard so many scary stories of people going blind etc. But again, I had complete confidence in Dr Olha and she made me feel totally at ease. I knew that she would never recommend a treatment that she didn't think was needed or wouldn't make an improvement. I know this because I have often asked about things and Dr Olha has reassured me that I don't need various treatments – she will only ever recommend something she thinks will help make an improvement or give the desired effect. Basically, what I'm trying to say here is that I don't feel like Dr Olha is doing this job just for the money, which is how other practitioners have made me feel in the past.

Would it have been useful to read a book about other people's experiences? If so, why?
I guess in hindsight it probably would have been. But I don't often read books, and so for me, bite-sized articles in magazines or social media posts might have held my attention better than a book. This is not to say I do not think it is a good idea. I think it is a wonderful idea, I just don't read often...

When you decided to go ahead, how did the treatment make you feel?
Botox: absolutely one million per cent better. Fresh-faced, with a youthful glow. Love it.

Tear trough filler: *love love love*, can't recommend this treatment enough. The one I least wanted but has made the biggest and *best* difference to my face.

Filler around the mouth: loved how this again made me feel more fresh and youthful.

Lip filler: I have mixed opinions – I think this is because I don't like the shape of my mouth, and sometimes it has felt like the filler just emphasises the shape of my top lip which I already don't like. Other times I have felt loads better with lip filler. When I feel my lips look a better shape is when the filler is in awkward places (sort of on the inside of my mouth) where they appear to blister or bulge a bit? I wonder whether I have damaged something around the border of my lips though? Because for me, sometimes the filler seems to be in my moustache area rather than in the pink part of my lips. (Perhaps leave this part out? More of a feedback note for Dr Olha I suppose.)

Would you continue to have the treatment and would you recommend it to other women?
Yes, and yes. I certainly would… and have, actually. I have introduced a few friends to Angels Twelve already and I am sure they have also introduced a couple more friends. It is well known that word-of-mouth marketing is the best form of marketing for any business, with over eighty per cent of people saying they would feel more confident buying a new product or service based on the recommendation of a friend, and aesthetics are a very personal thing, something you would really appreciate a friend's advice on.

One of my friends (Jenna, FYI) was always quite against the idea of injecting anything into her face, but when I showed her a before and after photo of my tear trough and told her how the Botox made me feel a hundred times better, she was completely sold.

Alexandra was so happy with the results that she provided her own before and after selfie, wouldn't you agree, she looks incredible?

Lisa

When/why did you first consider looking for advice on aesthetic or skin treatments?
I first considered and took advice when I reached the age of forty.

How long did it take you between considering treatment and booking a consultation?
A few days as I knew I was ready.

How did you research before calling to book?
I researched by speaking to a lot of friends who had previously had treatments and procedures. I also reviewed the website and took my time looking at all of the individual procedures to see which ones were right for me.

What factors were important to you when choosing your clinic?
First and foremost the practitioner – I knew I had to have an experienced, knowledgeable and highly recommended

practitioner with years of experience. I then had to factor in travel time with me working split shifts – this is also important to me.

Were you worried about having treatments? If so, why?
Yes I was a little anxious – with it being my face, I wanted to get the right treatment for me, so it was important to get the right clinic.

Would it have been useful to read a book about other people's experiences? If so, why?
Yes I do believe so, as I always read the reviews and love looking at before and after photos.

When you decided to go ahead, how did the treatment make you feel?
Wonderful, as soon as I've had the treatment I always feel so much better, more confident and happy.

Would you continue to have the treatment and would you recommend it to other women?
Absolutely – the difference that Olha has made to me is astonishing. I would highly recommend and always do so to my friends and colleagues.

References

1. https://www.surgery.org/sites/default/files/Stats2013_3.pdf
2. https://link.springer.com/referenceworkentry/10.1007/978-3-319-16802-9_28?noAccess=true
3. https://www.ncbi.nlm.nih.gov/pmc/articles/PMC4366708/
4. https://www.oatext.com/pdf/GOD-4-202.pdf
5. https://www.shinemedical.co.uk/treatments-prices/colum1/prp-therapy.html
6. https://www.thebeautyhavenleics.co.uk/leicester-beauty/led-therapy.html